PRIMARY MATHEMATICS

Challenging
Word Problems

Yan Kow Cheong

Marshall Cavendish
Education

© 2010 Panpac Education Private Limited
© 2011 Marshall Cavendish International (Singapore) Private Limited

This edition ©2014 Marshall Cavendish Education Pte Ltd

Published by Marshall Cavendish Education
Times Centre, 1 New Industrial Road, Singapore 536196
Customer Service Hotline: (65) 6213 9688
US Office Tel: (+1-914) 332 8888 | Fax: (+1-914) 332 8882
E-mail: cs@mceducation.com
Website: www.mceducation.com

First published 2010
New edition 2014
Reprinted 2014, 2015, 2017, 2018 (twice), 2019, 2020 (twice)

Primary Mathematics (Common Core Edition) Challenging Word Problems 3
ISBN 978-981-01-8973-0

Printed in Singapore

We would like to acknowledge contributions by:

Primary Mathematics (Common Core Edition) Challenging Word Problems
Jennifer Kempe (Curriculum Advisor from Singapore Math Inc.®)

Preface

Common Core Edition **Challenging Word Problems** provides graded exercises for students of mixed abilities and challenging questions for better math students. This series is written to supplement Singapore's **Primary Mathematics** textbooks (Common Core Edition) distributed by Singapore Math Inc.® for use in the USA.

Adopting a topical approach in which mathematical concepts and skills are taught and reinforced, the **Challenging Word Problems** series serves to improve students' problem-solving skills and enhance their mathematical reasoning.

Each book in the series features the following:

- **Worked Examples** for each topic show common methods of solution used in the Primary Mathematics textbooks;

- **Practice Questions** allow students to apply and practice questions similar to the ones discussed in the Worked Examples and in the Primary Mathematics textbooks;

- **Challenging Problems** provide opportunities for more capable students to solve higher-order word problems and further develop their problem-solving skills;

- **Review Questions** allow students to test their understanding of the concepts discussed in earlier topics and in the Primary Mathematics textbooks;

- **Answers** allow teachers or students to check their answers to all practice exercises and challenging problems;

- **Worked solutions** provide commonly used methods of solving non-routine questions, while encouraging creative or intuitive ones as well.

A student's guide to using the **Challenging Word Problems** series effectively.

1. Read each question given in the Worked Example. Try to solve it before reading the solution.

2. If your solution is similar to the one given in the Worked Example, well done. If you have used a different method, yet have arrived at the same answer, great—you now have at least two methods of solving this question.

3. If your answer is different, look at your work again and figure out where you may have gone wrong.

4. If you have understood all the worked examples, proceed to the Practice Questions; then check your answers with the ones at the back of the book. Should you get stuck at any question, don't panic; go through it again. If you still find difficulty in solving the question, seek help from your friend or teacher.

5. If you have understood and solved all the Practice Questions, you are now ready to try the Challenging Problems. Do them on your own first. Seek help only if you need some hints or clarification.

6. Try to come up with similar questions and challenge your friends to solve them. For a given question, discuss some possible solutions that you may have used in arriving at the answer.

Contents

1 Addition and Subtraction

Worked Example 1

Arthur scored 258 points at a carnival game. Joel scored 84 more points than Arthur and 68 more points than Ruth. How many points did the three children score in all?

258

Arthur

84

Joel

?

Ruth

68

Method 1

258 + 84 = 342
Joel scored 342 points.
342 − 68 = 274
Ruth scored 274 points.
258 + 342 + 274 = 874
The three children scored **874** points in all.

Method 2

258 + 258 + 258 + 84 + 84 − 68
= 774 + 168 − 68
= 874
The three children scored **874** points in all.

There is no need to find the score of Joel and of Ruth before finding the total score.

Worked Example 2

Ivan has 400 more stickers than Tom at first. He gives 300 stickers to Tom. Who has more stickers now? How many more?

Before

400

Ivan

Tom

After

100

Ivan

100   ?

Tom

300

400 − 300 = 100

300 − 100 = 200

Tom has **200** more stickers than Ivan now.

A common mistake is to take 400 − 300 = 100, and say that Ivan has 100 more stickers than Tom.

Worked Example 3

Sally had 57 more pencils than pens. After she gave away 47 pencils, she had twice as many pencils as pens. How many pens and pencils did Sally have left altogether?

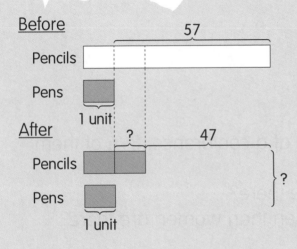

Method 1

1 unit = 57 − 47 = 10
3 units = 3 × 10 = 30
Sally had **30** pens and pencils left altogether.

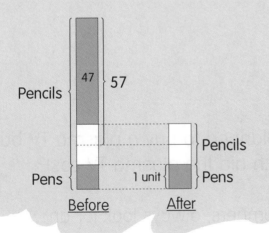

Method 2

1 unit = 57 − 47 = 10
3 units = 3 × 10 = 30
Sally had **30** pens and pencils left altogether.

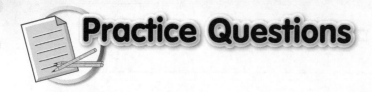

Practice Questions

Answer all questions. Show your work and write your statements clearly.

1. Joel collected 4,352 stamps. He had 469 fewer stamps than Mark. How many stamps did Mark collect?

2. There are 2,450 adults at a conference. 896 of them are women.
    (a) How many men are there?
    (b) How many more men than women are there?

3. Mr. Albert had $997. He planned to buy a plasma TV but was short $498. How much did the plasma TV cost?

    Hint: In adding two large numbers, always look for an effective (or shorter) way to do this.

4. How many times does the digit "0" appear in numbers from 1 to 100?

   Hint: Use a systematic list.

5. A movie theater has 1,210 seats. During the first movie showtime, 947 seats were taken. During the second showtime, there were 139 empty seats. How many people watched the two showtimes altogether?

   Hint: See Worked Example 1.

6. Steve has 500 more marbles than Richard at first. He gives 300 marbles to Richard. Who has more marbles now, and by how many?

   Caution: Draw a model to visualize the problem situation.

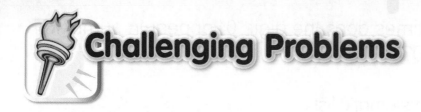

Challenging Problems

Worked Example 1

I am thinking of a four-digit number. When I add all the digits, the sum is 17. What is the smallest possible number?

(Do not begin the number with the digit "0".)

Step 1:

Let the thousands digit be 1 and the hundreds digit be 0.

thousands	hundreds	tens	ones
1	0		

Step 2:

$$\underbrace{1 + 0}_{1} + \underbrace{\text{tens digit} + \text{ones digit}}_{16} = 17$$

$16 = 7 + 9$
$16 = 8 + 8$
$16 = 9 + 7$

Step 3:

$1 + 0 + 7 + 9 = 17$

Note that for the smallest possible number, the tens digit must be 7 and not 9.

The smallest possible number is **1,079**.

Extension: What would be the largest possible number I am thinking about?

Worked Example 2

Dennis wrote all the numbers from 300 to 400 on a notebook. How many times did he write the digit "3"?

Number	Number of "3"s
300, 301, …, 399	100 (in the hundreds place)
330, 331, …, 339	10 (in the tens place)
303, 313, …, 393	10 (in the ones place)

$100 + 10 + 10 = 120$

He wrote the digit "3" **120** times.

Note: We do the counting in a systematic way, instead of randomly counting the 3s.

Note that
$99 - 0 + 1 = 100$
$9 - 0 + 1 = 10.$

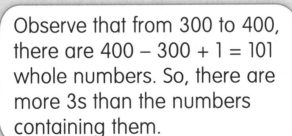

Observe that from 300 to 400, there are $400 - 300 + 1 = 101$ whole numbers. So, there are more 3s than the numbers containing them.

Answer all questions. Show your work and write your statements clearly.

1. The sum of P and Q is 1,023 greater than Q. The sum of P and Q is 549 greater than P.
   (a) What is the value of P?
   (b) What is the value of Q?
   (c) What is the sum of P and Q?

   Hint: Draw a diagram to visualize each situation.

2. Laval is 18 years older than Chris. How old will Chris be when Laval is three times as old as Chris?

   Hint: The age difference between Laval and Chris remains unchanged.

3. Jerry and Rick collect toy cars. Rick has 12 more toy cars than Jerry. They have 38 toy cars altogether. How many toy cars does Jerry have in his collection?

   Hint: Draw a model to visualize the situation.

4. How many times does the digit "9" appear in the numbers from 1 to 100?

   Hint: Remember to count the numbers in the nineties.

5. The letters P, Q, R, and S stand for a one-digit number each.

$$\begin{array}{r} P\ Q \\ +\ R\ S \\ \hline 1\ 5\ 9 \end{array}$$

   What is the value of P + Q + R + S?

   Hint: You do not need to know the value of each letter, yet you can find their sum.

6. Alberta saw 15 wild cats and flamingoes at the zoo. She counted their legs and found that there were 44 legs altogether. How many wild cats did she see at the zoo?

   Hint: There is more than one method of solution. Try to solve the question in as many ways as possible such as guess and check, make an assumption.

7. Abel saved 43 more nickels than dimes. After he spent 17 dimes, he had twice as many nickels than dimes. How many coins did he have left?

   5¢

   10¢

8. A baker sold a total of 1,320 loaves of bread in June and July. He sold 678 loaves in June and 901 loaves in August. How many more loaves did he sell in August than in July?

   Hint: Use a model to make the comparison easier to see.

9. How many whole numbers between 1 and 100 contain the digit "6"?

   Hint: Remember the numbers whose tens digit is 6.

10. You have a sheet of stamps. The stamps are connected in 5 rows, each with 5 stamps. What is the least number of times you can tear the sheet to get all the stamps apart?

   Hint: The stamps can be torn apart at the perforations between them. Several layers of stamps can be torn apart at one time if the perforations are lined up.

Multiplication and Division

Worked Example 1

> Each boy has 7 stickers and each girl has 6 stickers. How many stickers do 9 boys and 8 girls have in total?

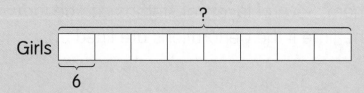

Boys

7

$9 \times 7 = 63$

9 boys have 63 stickers.

Girls

6

$8 \times 6 = 48$

8 girls have 48 stickers.

$63 + 48 = 111$

9 boys and 8 girls have **111** stickers in total.

Worked Example 2

A total of 348 pears are put equally into 6 boxes. If 19 pears are removed from one box, how many pears are left in that box?

Method 1

348 ÷ 6 = 58

There are 58 pears in each box.

58 − 19 = 39

39 pears are left in that box.

Method 2

$$348 = 300 + 48$$
$$= 6 \times 50 + 6 \times 8$$

50 + 8 = 58

Each box has 58 pears.

$$58 - 19 = 58 - 18 - 1$$
$$= 40 - 1$$
$$= 39$$

39 pears are left in that box

13

Worked Example 3

Mrs. Azikou has 9 albums with 108 stamps each. She rearranges all the stamps equally into 6 larger albums. How many stamps will there be in each of the larger albums?

$9 \times 108 = 972$

There are 972 stamps altogether.

$972 \div 6 = 162$

There will be **162** stamps in each of the larger albums.

Answer all questions. Show your work and write your statements clearly.

1. Each student receives 6 coins and each teacher receives 7 coins. How many coins do 8 students and 5 teachers receive altogether?

2. Mrs. Mendez and Miss Holders distributed 120 pens equally among 8 children. How many pens did each child receive?

3. Mr. Golbout arranged 544 apples equally into 8 boxes. If he took out 29 apples from one box, how many apples would be left in that box?

4. Mr. Levoko has 7 bags of 126 coins each. He transfers all the coins into 3 bigger bags. How many coins will each bigger bag contain?

5. Bobby has 345 postcards. He gives 36 postcards to each of his 4 cousins. How many postcards does he have left?

6. Steve has 32 stickers. Joe has three times as many stickers as Steve but half as many stickers as Arlette. How many stickers does Arlette have?

7. Each album has 120 stamps. In each album, there are 42 Canada stamps, 50 U.S. stamps and the rest are Mexico stamps. How many Mexico stamps do 6 such albums have in total?

8. For every paper crane Ann makes, Sally can make 2 paper cranes. If they make 141 paper cranes altogether, how many paper cranes are made by Sally?

Challenging Problems

Worked Example 1

Elsa and Mary collected a total of 20 empty bottles.
For every 2 empty bottles Elsa collected, Mary collected 3.
How many empty bottles did each girl collect?

Method 1

Elsa	Mary	Total
2	3	5
4	6	10
6	9	15
8	12	20

From the table, Elsa collected **8** empty bottles and
Mary collected **12** empty bottles.

Method 2

2 + 3 = 5 ⟶ 1 group of 5 bottles
20 ÷ 5 = 4

There are 4 groups of 5 bottles.
4 × 2 = 8 and 4 × 3 = 12

Elsa collected **8** empty bottles and Mary collected
12 empty bottles.

Worked Example 2

Gregory has 480 stamps. Steven has 260 stamps. How many stamps must Gregory give to Steven so that they have the same number of stamps? How many stamps will each of them have after sharing?

Method 1

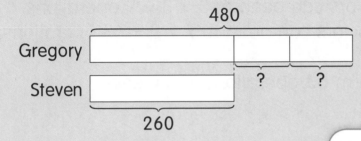

480 − 260 = 220

220 ÷ 2 = 110

Gregory must give Steven **110** stamps.

> There is a difference of 220 stamps.

480 − 110 = 370 and 260 + 110 = 370

Each of them will have **370** stamps after sharing.

Method 2

Total number of stamps = 480 + 260

= 740

740 ÷ 2 = 370

Each of them will have **370** stamps after sharing.

480 − 370 = 110   or   370 − 260 = 110

Gregory must give Steven **110** stamps.

Worked Example 3

Dr. Sumo and his 2 colleagues each can perform 3 operations every day. How many operations can they perform in a week?

Dr. Sumo and his 2 colleagues make up 3 doctors.

In 1 day, 3 doctors can perform 3 × 3 = 9 operations.
In 7 days, 3 doctors can perform 7 × 9 = 63 operations.

They can perform **63** operations in a week.

Answer all questions. Show your work and write your statements clearly.

1. Mrs. Smith goes into a store and orders a total of 85 blue and green balloons for her daughter's birthday. However, she wants 25 more green than blue balloons. How many balloons of each color will she take home?

2. Adam had 568 postcards and his sister, Sue, had 384 postcards. Adam gave Sue some postcards so they now have the same number. How many postcards do each of them have now?

3. A train that serves two remote villages is 142 meters long. It has 8 cars, each 16 meters long. What is the distance between two neighboring cars, if the distance between the cars is the same?

   Hint: Draw a diagram to visualize the length of the entire train.

4. A bus can carry 48 passengers. How many buses will be needed to carry 120 passengers? How many seats will be unoccupied?

   Hint: How many groups of 48 passengers can go into 120 buses?

5. Mrs. Jiminez gave some students 4 candies each. She then had 8 candies left. How many students received candies from Mrs. Jiminez if she had 84 candies at first?

   Hint: How many candies were given away?

6. After giving 16 coins to Melissa, Juan had twice as many coins as Melissa. If they had 144 coins altogether, how many coins did Juan have at first?

7. Rita had 24 more barrettes than Zoe. After she gave 5 barrettes to Zoe, Rita had twice as many barrettes as Zoe. How many barettes did Rita have left?

8. Jason and Louis picked up a total of 30 cans. For every 2 cans that Jason picked up, Louis picked up 3 cans. How many cans did each boy pick up?

9. There are some red envelopes containing 6 stamps each. There are also some blue envelopes containing 5 stickers each. What is the least possible number of red envelopes and blue envelopes that have as many stamps as stickers?

Hint: Guess and check. The total numbers of stamps in all red envelopes and blue envelopes are the same.

10. In order to make a rock bear, 1 large rock is used for the body and 5 small rocks are used for the head and legs. Jack has 9 large rocks and 20 small rocks. How many rock bears can he make?

Hint: Not all the rocks may be used to form the rock bears.

3 Mental Calculation

Worked Example 1

Add the following mentally.
(a) 28 + 9
(b) 157 + 99

(a) $28 + 9 = 28 + 10 - 1$
$= 38 - 1$
$= \mathbf{37}$

Look for "friendly numbers" like 10 and 100.
$9 = 10 - 1$
$99 = 100 - 1$

(b) **Method 1**

$157 + 99 = 157 + 100 - 1$
$= 257 - 1$
$= \mathbf{256}$

Method 2

$157 + 99 = 156 + 1 + 99$
$= 156 + 100$
$= \mathbf{256}$

Worked Example 2

Calculate the following subtractions mentally.
(a) 187 − 98
(b) 705 − 399

(a) **Method 1**

$$187 - 98 = 187 - 100 + 2$$
$$= 87 + 2$$
$$= \textbf{89}$$

Method 2

$$187 - 98 = 189 - 100$$
$$= \textbf{89}$$

Increase both numbers by 2.

(b) **Method 1**

$$705 - 399 = 706 - 400$$
$$= \textbf{306}$$

Method 2

$$705 - 399 = 705 - 300 - 99$$
$$= 405 - 99$$
$$= 405 - 100 + 1$$
$$= 305 + 1$$
$$= \textbf{306}$$

Increase both numbers by 1.

```
        399
       /    \
    300      99
```

Can you think of other methods to subtract mentally?

Worked Example 3

Multiply the following mentally.
(a) 45 × 6   (b) 607 × 8
(c) 25 × 9

(a) **Method 1**

$$45 \times 6 = 40 \times 6 + 5 \times 6$$
$$= 240 + 30$$
$$= \mathbf{270}$$

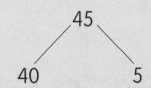

Method 2

$$45 \times 6 = 40 \times 2 \times 3$$
$$= 90 \times 3$$
$$= \mathbf{270}$$

(b) $607 \times 8 = 600 \times 8 + 7 \times 8$
$$= 4,800 + 56$$
$$= \mathbf{4,856}$$

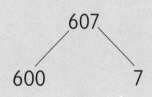

(c) **Method 1**

$$25 \times 9 = 25 \times 10 - 25 \times 1$$
$$= 250 - 25$$
$$= \mathbf{225}$$

Look for "friendly numbers" like 10 and 100.
$9 = 10 - 1$

Method 2

$$25 \times 9 = 20 \times 9 + 5 \times 9$$
$$= 180 + 45$$
$$= \mathbf{225}$$

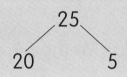

Practice Questions

Answer all questions.

Do the following mentally.

1. $56 + 9$

2. $728 + 98$

3. $145 - 99$

4. $706 - 198$

5. 505×9

6. 82×6

7. $198 + 243$

8. $752 - 303$

9. 57×3

Challenging Problems

Worked Example 1

Add the following mentally.

(a) 137 + 48 + 63
(b) 56 + 36 + 68
(c) 488 + 356
(d) 998 + 703

(a) 137 + 48 + 63
   = 137 + 63 + 48
   = 200 + 48
   = **248**

Add "friendly numbers" first.

(b) 56 + 36 + 68
   = 56 + 30 + 4 + 2 + 68
   = 56 + 4 + 30 + 2 + 68
   = 60 + 30 + 70
   = **160**

Look for an easier addition.

(c) 488 + 356
   = 488 + 12 + 344
   = 500 + 344
   = **844**

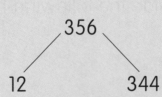

356
12   344

(d) 998 + 703
   = 998 + 2 + 701
   = 1,000 + 701
   = **1,701**

703
2   701

Worked Example 2

Subtract the following mentally.

(a) 6,000 − 348   (b) 142 − 80   (c) 142 − 85

(a) 6,000 − 348 = $\underbrace{5,999 - 348}$ + 1

$6,000 = 5,999 + 1$

= 5,651 + 1

= **5,652**

(b) 142 − 80 = 42 + $\underbrace{100 - 80}$

= 42 + 20

= **62**

(c) 142 − 85 = 42 + $\underbrace{100 - 85}$

= 42 + 15

= **57**

Worked Example 3

Multiply or divide the following mentally.

(a) 46 × 5   (b) 165 × 5
(c) 38 ÷ 2   (d) 190 ÷ 5

(a) 46 × 5 = 46 × 10 ÷ 2

$5 = 10 \div 2$

= 460 ÷ 2

= **230**

(b) $165 \times 5 = 165 \times 10 \div 2$
$= 1,650 \div 2$
$= \mathbf{825}$

(c) **Method 1**

$38 \div 2 = 40 \div 2 - 2 \div 2$
$= 20 - 1$
$= \mathbf{19}$

$38 = 40 - 2$

Method 2

$38 \div 2 = 30 \div 2 + 8 \div 2$
$= 15 + 4$
$= \mathbf{19}$

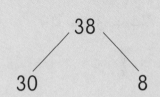

38

30   8

(d) $190 \div 5 = 190 \times 2 \div 5 \times 2$
$= 380 \div 10$
$= \mathbf{38}$

Multiply both numbers by 2.

Can you use other methods to multiply or divide mentally?

Answer all questions.

Do the following mentally.

1. 158 + 93 + 42

2. 997 + 605

3. 74 + 37 + 49

4. 234 + 567

5. 7,000 − 137

6. 10,000 − 894

7. 126 − 75

8. 163 − 92

9. 58 × 2

10. 750 × 2

11. 92 ÷ 2

12. 740 ÷ 2

13. 85 × 5

14. 462 × 5

15. 620 ÷ 5

16. 905 ÷ 5

4 Length

Worked Example 1

Sam and Jim have a total height of 3 m 27 cm. If Sam is 1 m 80 cm tall, how much taller is he than Jim?

Method 1

	1 m 80 cm	
Sam		
Jim		?

3 m 27 cm

3 m 27 cm – 1 m 80 cm = 1 m 47 cm
Jim is 1 m 47 cm.
1 m 80 cm – 1 m 47 cm = 33 cm
Sam is **33 cm** taller than Jim.

Method 2

1 m 80 cm + 1 m 80 cm = 2 m 160 cm
                      = 3 m 60 cm
3 m 60 cm – 3 m 27 cm = 33 cm
Sam is **33 cm** taller than Jim.

Worked Example 2

Dave and Joy have a total height of 8 ft 9 in. Joy and Rick have a total height of 8 ft 4 in. If Rick is 4 ft 6 in. tall, what is the height of Dave? Express your answer in feet and inches.

Joy is shorter than Rick since 8 ft 4 in. − 4 ft 6 in. = 3 ft 10 in.
Dave is taller than Joy since 8 ft 9 in. − 3 ft 10 in. = 4 ft 11 in.

Note: Although a diagram or model to show the problem situation is not necessary, it does help one to better visualize the situation. Notice also that the statements on their own do not tell us who is taller or shorter, until we take the difference in heights.

Method 1

8 ft 4 in. − 4 ft 6 in. = 3 ft 10 in.
Joy is 3 ft 10 in. tall.
8 ft 9 in. − 3 ft 10 in. = 4 ft 11 in.
Dave is **4 ft 11 in.** tall.

Method 2

4 ft 6 in. + 8 ft 9 in. = 13 ft 3 in.
The total height of Dave, Joy, and Rick is **13 ft 3 in.**
13 ft 3 in. − 8 ft 4 in. = 4 ft 11 in.
Dave is **4 ft 11 in.** tall.

Worked Example 3

Town X and town Y are 4 km 225 m apart. Town Y and town Z are 3 km 550 m apart. Roy drove from town Z to town Y, then to town X. Finally, he drove back to town Y. What was the total distance Roy traveled in kilometers?

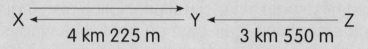

X ←⎯⎯⎯⎯⎯⎯→ Y ←⎯⎯⎯ Z
    4 km 225 m   3 km 550 m

Journey	Distance traveled
From town Z to town Y	3 km 550 m
From town Y to town X	4 km 225 m
From town X to town Y	4 km 225 m

3 km 550 m + 4 km 225 m + 4 km 225 m = 12 km

The total distance Roy traveled was **12 km.**

 **Practice Questions**

Answer all questions. Show your work and write your statements clearly.

1. Henry is 1 m 65 cm tall. Charles is 16 cm taller than Henry but 8 cm shorter than Albert. How tall is Albert? Give your answer in meters and centimeters.

2. Robin bought a string that is 3 m 25 cm long. He used 1 m 65 cm of the string to tie a box and another 1 m 25 cm to tie a pebble. What length of string did he have left?

3. String P is twice as long as string Q. String R is three times as long as string P. Strings P, Q, and R have a total length of 495 cm. What is the length of string R?

   Hint: Look for the shortest string, and represent its length by one unit.

4. String A is twice as long as string B. String C is three times as long as string B. The total length of the three strings is 624 cm. What is the length of string A? Express your answer in meters and centimeters.

   Hint: To compare the strings, draw a model. Out of the three strings, which one is the shortest? Represent it by one unit.

5. The total height of Lisa and Claire is 2 m 80 cm.
   The total height of Claire and Yvonne is 2 m 95 cm.
   If Yvonne's height is 1 m 45 cm, how tall is Lisa?
   Express your answer in meters and centimeters.

   Hint: 1 meter = 100 centimeters

6. Adeline and Kelly have a total height of 10 ft 2 in. If Adeline is 5 ft 4 in. tall, find Kelly's height. Who is taller: Adeline or Kelly, and by how much?

   Hint: 1 foot = 12 inches.

7. The total length of string P and string Q is 818 cm. String P is 342 cm shorter than string Q. What is the length of string Q in meters and centimeters?

   Think: How would you solve this problem by taking the length of P as one unit instead?

8. Farmer George planted 9 trees along one side of his farm. The distance between every two neighboring trees is 120 cm. What is the distance between the first tree and the last tree? Express your answer in meters and centimeters.

   Hint: How many intervals are there along one side?

Challenging Problems

Worked Example 1

There are 30 trees along a straight road. Any two neighboring trees are 10 m apart. What is the distance between the third tree and the third last tree?

28 − 3 = 25 intervals

10 m   10 m   10 m   10 m   10 m

3rd   4th   28th   29th   30th
tree   tree   tree   tree   tree

3rd last tree

Method 1

The interval between two neighboring trees is 10 m long. Between the 3rd tree and the 3rd last tree (28th tree), there are 28 − 3 = 25 intervals.
25 intervals have a length of 25 × 10 m = 250 m.
The distance between the third tree and the third last tree is **250 m**.

Method 2

From the 1st to the 3rd tree, there are 2 intervals.
From the 3rd last tree to the last tree, there are also 2 intervals.
From the 1st to the 30th tree, there are 29 intervals.
From the 3rd to the 3rd last tree, there are 29 − 2 − 2 = 25 intervals.
Each interval is 10 m long.
25 intervals are 10 × 25 = 250 m long.
The distance between the third tree and the third last tree is **250 m**.

Worked Example 2

String P is twice as long as string Q. After 75 cm of string P is cut off, string P is half as long as string Q. What is the total length of both strings at first?

Method 1

Before

String Q

String P

?

After

String Q

String P

75 cm

3 units = 75 cm
  1 unit = 75 cm ÷ 3 = 25 cm
6 units = 6 × 25 cm = 150 cm
Both strings have a total length of **150 cm** at first.

Method 2

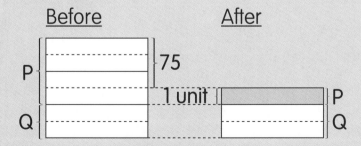

From the model,
3 units = 75 cm
6 units = 2 × 75 cm = 150 cm
Both strings have a total length of **150 cm** at first.

Answer all questions. Show your work and write your statements clearly.

1. A pink ribbon was twice as long as a white ribbon. When 2 m 30 cm of the pink ribbon was cut off, the remainder was still 3 m 40 cm longer than the white ribbon. How long was the pink ribbon at first? Express your answer in meters and centimeters.

2. There are 15 lamp posts along a stretch of road. The distance between 2 neighboring lamp posts is 500 m. What is the distance between the sixth and third last lamp posts? Express your answer in kilometers and meters.

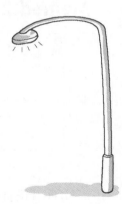

3. Ribbon X was three times as long as ribbon Y. After 120 ft of ribbon X was cut off, ribbon X was twice as long as ribbon Y. What was the total length (in yards) of ribbons X and Y at first?

4. Bob is 5 ft 6 in. tall. Mark is 4 ft 7 in. tall. Their total height is 3 in. more than the total height of June and Anne. If June is 4 ft 9 in. tall, what is the height of Anne? Express your answer in feet and inches.

5. String A is 1 yd shorter than string B. String C is 1 ft 8 in. shorter than string B. The total length of the three strings is 13 ft 4 in. What is the length of string A?

Hint: 1 yd = 3 feet.

6. A piece of wire 480 cm long is bent to form a triangle of equal sides. What is the length of each side of the triangle in meters and centimeters?

7. String P is 42 cm longer than string Q. String R is 68 cm longer than string Q. The total length of strings P, Q, and R is 320 cm. What is the total length of strings P and Q? Express your answer in meters and centimeters.

8. Stick A is 120 cm shorter than stick B. Stick C is 84 cm shorter than stick B. Sticks A, B, and C have a total length of 360 cm. What is the total length (in meters and centimeters) of sticks A and C?

5 Mass and Weight

Worked Example 1

The total mass of a watermelon and a guava is 1 kg 700 g. The watermelon is 930 g heavier than the guava. What is the mass of each fruit?

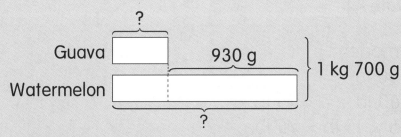

1 kg 700 g – 930 g = 770 g

770 g ÷ 2 = 385 g

The guava has a mass of **385 g**.

385 g + 930 g = 1 kg 315 g

or

1 kg 700 g – 385 g = 1 kg 315 g

The watermelon has a mass of **1 kg 315 g**.

Worked Example 2

Crate Q weighs three times as much as crate P. Crate P weighs twice as much as crate R. If crate Q is 60 lb heavier than crate P, how much heavier is crate Q than crate R?

Crate P [____|____]

Crate Q [__|__|__|__|__|__] 60 lb

Crate R [____] ?

From the model,
4 units = 60 lb
1 unit = 60 lb ÷ 4 = 15 lb
5 units = 5 × 15 lb = 75 lb.

Crate Q is **75 lb** heavier than crate R.

Worked Example 3

Eve has 142 g of rice. Mary has 170 g of rice and Ian has 396 g of rice. What is the total mass of rice that Ian must give to Eve and Mary altogether so that each of them has the same amount of rice?

```
                    142 g
           ┌──────────────────────┐
   Eve     │                      │
           ├──────────────────────────┐
  Mary     │                          │
           └──────────────────────────┘
                       170 g

           ┌──────────────────────────────────────┐
   Ian     │                                      │
           └──────────────────────────────────────┘
                          396 g
```

142 g + 170 g + 396 g = 708 g

Eve, Mary, and Ian have a total of 708 g of rice.

708 g ÷ 3 = 236 g

If the rice is divided equally among Eve, Mary, and 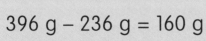 Ian, each of them will have 236 g of rice.

396 g – 236 g = 160 g

Ian must give **160 g** of rice to Eve and Mary altogether so that each of them will have the same amount of rice.

Practice Questions

Answer all questions. Show your work and write your statements clearly.

1. The total mass of a melon and a pear is 1 kg 550 g. The melon is 720 g heavier than the pear. What is the mass of the pear?

    Hint: See Worked Example 1. Which of the two methods works better here?

2. The total weight of a box of 9 apples is 3 lb. Each apple weighs 5 oz. What is the weight of the box?

3. Peter weighs 104 lb. Lisa is half as heavy as Peter. Timothy is 10 lb lighter than Lisa. How much does Timothy weigh?

4. The total weight of George and Tom is 248 lb. If George is 36 lb lighter than Tom, what is Tom's weight?

5. The mass of a guava is 555 g. It is three times as heavy as an apple. What is the total mass of the guava and the apple?

6. Bag B is four times as heavy as bag A. Bag A is three times as heavy as bag C. If bag A is 180 g lighter than bag B, how much lighter is bag C than bag B?

7. Ten full crates of peanuts have a mass of 220 kg while an empty crate weighs 5 kg. What is the mass of the peanuts in each crate?

8. June has 456 g of flour, Ann has 210 g of flour, and Joyce has 306 g of flour. How much flour must June give to Ann and Joyce in order that each of them has the same amount of flour?

   Hint: See Worked Example 3.

9. The weight of Sue's bag is 20 lb 5 oz. Charlene's bag is 2 lb 10 oz lighter than Sue's bag. Keith's bag is 4 lb 6 oz heavier than Charlene's bag. What is the weight (in pounds and ounces) of Keith's bag?

Challenging Problems

Worked Example 1

Albert, Paul, and Jane have a total mass of 123 kg. Albert's mass is 32 kg. Paul is twice as heavy as Albert.
(a) What is Paul's mass?
(b) What is Jane's mass?

(a)

32 kg

Albert

Paul

?

$2 \times 32 \text{ kg} = 64 \text{ kg}$
Paul's mass is **64 kg**.

(b)

32 kg

Albert

Paul

123 kg

64 kg

Jane

?

$32 \text{ kg} + 64 \text{ kg} = 96 \text{ kg}$
Albert and Paul have a total mass of 96 kg.

$123 \text{ kg} - 96 \text{ kg} = 27 \text{ kg}$
Jane's mass is **27 kg**.

Note: When drawing the bar representing Jane's mass, it is not possible to determine immediately whether it is longer or shorter than the bar representing Albert's mass.

Worked Example 2

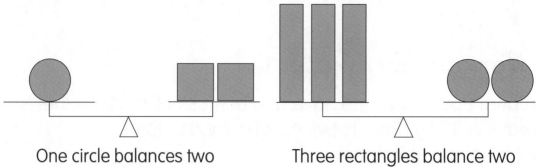

One circle balances two squares.

Three rectangles balance two circles.

Each circle weighs 90 g.
(a) What is the mass of the square?
(b) What is the mass of the rectangle?
(c) How many squares and rectangles will balance both sides of the scales?

(a) 2 squares have a mass of 90 g.
   1 square has a mass of 90 g ÷ 2 = **45 g**.

(b) 3 rectangles have a mass as much as 2 circles.
   3 rectangles have a mass of 2 × 90 g = 180 g.
   1 rectangle has a mass of 180 g ÷ 3 = **60 g**.

(c)

Number of squares	Total mass (g)	Number of rectangles	Total mass (g)
1	45	1	60
2	90	2	120
3	135	3	(180)
4	(180)		

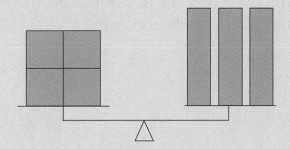

4 squares and **3 rectangles** will balance both sides of the scales.

Extension: If more squares and rectangles were to be added on both sides of the scales, how many more of each shape would be needed to balance the scales?

Answer all questions. Show your work and write your statements clearly.

1. The mass of a pineapple is 880 g. The pineapple has a mass 3 times more than an orange. What is the total mass of the pineapple and the orange? Express your answer in kilograms and grams.

   Hint: The pineapple has a mass three times more, not three times as much, as the oranges.

2. In the diagram below, what is the mass of X?

	50 g	20 g				
50 g	X	100 g		200 g	100 g	20 g
200 g	200 g	500 g		200 g	200 g	500 g

3. Mrs. Yong buys the following items at the supermarket.

Item	Mass
Fish	725 g
Cucumber	310 g
Carrots	275 g
Beef	1 kg 350 g
Watermelon	530 g
Cabbage	290 g

Express all your answers in kilograms and grams.
(a) What is the total mass of the lightest and the heaviest items?
(b) What is the total mass of all the items?
(c) If her son offers to help carry the meat, what is the total mass of the remaining items Mrs.Yong needs to carry?

4. Bag A weighs 64 lb and bag B weighs 18 lb less than bag A. Bag C is twice as heavy as the total weight of bags A and B. What is the weight of bag C?

5. Box C is twice as heavy as box B. The weight of box A is two times more than the weight of box C. If box B weighs 90 lb, what is the weight of box A?

6. The mass of item A is 1 kg 500 g. Item B is 310 g lighter than item A. Item C is 435 g less than item B.
   (a) What is the mass of item B?
   (b) What is the mass of item C?
   (c) What is the difference in mass between items A and C?

7. The total mass of Ann, Lisa, and Karen is 101 kg. Lisa's mass is 56 kg. Ann has a mass that is half as much as Lisa.

(a) What is Ann's mass?

(b) What is Karen's mass?

8.

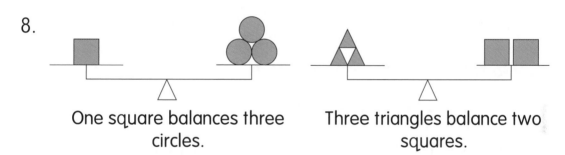

One square balances three circles.

Three triangles balance two squares.

How many circles and triangles will balance both sides of the scales?

Hint: See Worked Example 2.

6 Capacity

Worked Example 1

A container has 625 mL of water. When 1 L 82 mL of water is poured into it, 107 mL of water overflows. What is the capacity of the container? Express your answer in liters and milliliters.

1 L 82 mL – 107 mL = 975 mL

975 mL of water is needed to fill the container.

625 mL + 975 mL = 1 L 600 mL

The capacity of the container is **1 L 600 mL**.

Note: There is a difference between the terms "capacity" and "volume". For example, a container has capacity one liter (the amount of space inside it) and the volume of water in the container is one liter (the actual amount of water inside it).

Worked Example 2

A tank is filled with 3 gal 3 qt of water. After 1 gal 1 qt of water is added into it, the tank is half filled. What is the capacity of the tank?

1 gal = 4 qt

3 gal 3 qt + 1 gal 1 qt = 5 gal

Half the tank contains 5 gal of water.

The whole tank can hold $2 \times 5 = 10$ gal of water.

The capacity of the tank is **10 gal**.

Worked Example 3

A jug contains 2 L 140 mL of orange juice. 1 L 360 mL of the orange juice is poured into 2 bottles and the rest is poured equally into 3 cups. How much orange juice does each cup contain?

2 L 140 mL – 1 L 360 mL = 780 mL

780 mL of orange juice is poured equally into 3 cups.

780 mL ÷ 3 = 260 mL

Each cup contains **260 mL** of orange juice.

Practice Questions

Answer each question carefully. Show your work and write your statement clearly.

1. A jug can hold 2 L 250 mL of water. A bottle can hold 1 L 340 mL less water than the jug. What is the total volume of water that both containers can hold? Express your answer in liters and milliliters.

2. A tank is filled to the brim with water. After 83 gal of water has been removed from it and another 29 gal added to it, the tank is half filled. What is the capacity of the tank?

3. An empty container has a capacity of 10 L. Paul adds 3 L 450 mL of water into it and Mary adds another 4 L 570 mL of water into it. How much more water can the container hold? Express your answer in liters and milliliters.

4. Jug A has 3 pt of water. Jug B has four times as much water as jug A but has 3 qt less water than jug C. What is the volume of water in jug C? Express your answer in gallons and quarts.

Hint: 1 qt = 2 pt; 1 gal = 4 qt.

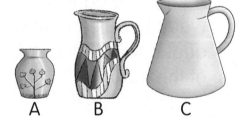

A B   C

5. Oliver adds 370 mL of concentrated apple juice and 290 mL of concentrated pear syrup to 8 L 450 mL of water to make some punch for a party. How much punch does he make in all? Express your answer in liters and milliliters.

Apple   Pear
juice   juice

6. A pail had 3 L 485 mL of water. When 2 L 108 mL of water was poured into it, 93 mL of water overflowed. What is the capacity of the pail? Express your answer in liters and milliliters.

Hint: See Worked Example 1.

Challenging Problems

Worked Example 1

Jill and Jack took turns to pour milk into a container. Jill used a 120-mL pail and Jack used a 150-mL pail. They stopped when they had poured the same volume of milk into the container.

(a) Find the number of times each had poured milk into the container.

(b) How much milk was poured into the container in all?

(a)

Jill: 120 mL

Number of times	Volume of milk
1	120
2	240
3	360
4	480
5	600

Jack: 150 mL

Number of times	Volume of milk
1	150
2	300
3	450
4	600
5	750

Jill poured **5** times.   Jack poured **4** times.

(b) 600 mL + 600 mL = 1 L 200 mL

1 L 200 mL milk was poured into the container in all.

Worked Example 2

One can and two bottles of *Fizzy Pop* have a total capacity of 410 mL. Two cans and one bottle of *Fizzy Pop* have a total capacity of 370 mL. Find the capacity of
(a) one can of *Fizzy Pop*,
(b) one bottle of *Fizzy Pop*.

Method 1

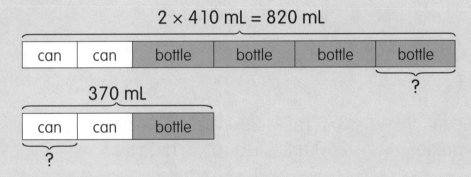

2 × 410 mL = 820 mL

| can | can | bottle | bottle | bottle | bottle |

370 mL

| can | can | bottle |

Capacity of 3 bottles: 820 mL − 370 mL = 450 mL
Capacity of 1 bottle: 450 mL ÷ 3 = 150 mL

Capacity of 2 cans: 370 mL − 150 mL = 220 mL
Capacity of 1 can: 220 mL ÷ 2 = 110 mL

(a) The capacity of one can of *Fizzy Pop* is **110 mL**.

(b) The capacity of one bottle of *Fizzy Pop* is **150 mL**.

Remember to check your answers!

Method 2

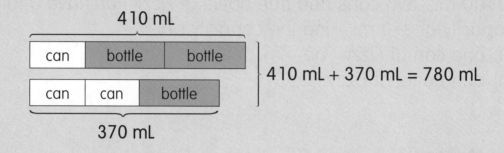

410 mL + 370 mL = 780 mL

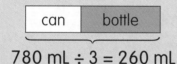

780 mL ÷ 3 = 260 mL

1 can ⟶ 370 mL − 260 mL = 110 mL
1 bottle ⟶ 260 mL − 110 mL = 150 mL

(a) The capacity of one can of *Fizzy Pop* is **110 mL**.

(b) The capacity of one bottle of *Fizzy Pop* is **150 mL**.

Can you use another method to solve the problem?

Answer all questions. Show your work and write your statements clearly.

1. One plastic container and two bottles can hold 920 mL of liquid detergent. Two plastic containers and one bottle can hold 850 mL of liquid detergent. Find the capacity of
    (a) one plastic container,
    (b) one bottle.

    Hint: See Worked Example 2.

2. Pails A and B have capacities of 3 liters and 7 liters respectively. Use these 2 pails to measure out
    (a) 1 liter of water,
    (b) 5 liters of water.

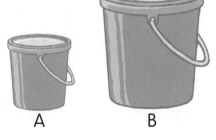

A   B

3. David and Ruth took turns to pour water into a pail. David used a 100-milliliter cup and Ruth used a 120-milliliter cup. They stopped when they had poured the same volume of water into the pail.
   (a) How many cups of water did each pour into the pail?
   (b) What was the total volume of water that was poured into the pail?

   Hint: See Worked Example 1.

4. Mrs. Vinny mixes equal amounts of liquid X and liquid Y to prepare her secret soup. One can contain 100 mL of liquid X. How many cans of liquid X must she buy to prepare 2 L of soup?

5. Four jugs and four buckets can hold a total of 50 gal of water. Each jug can hold 2 qt of water. What is the capacity of 3 buckets?

6. Half a jug of water can fill exactly 5 glasses. Each glass has a capacity of 250 mL. Find the capacity of 4 jugs in liters.

7. Pails A, B and C have capacities of 3 L, 5 L and 8 L respectively. How can you use these 3 pails to measure out 4 L of water?

   Hint: What is the least number of steps needed to achieve this?

8. The total capacity of a pail and a jug is 10 L. The capacity of a pail is 9 L more than that of the jug. What is the capacity of the jug in milliliters?

9. Joel has a jar containing 220 mL of water. Elisa has a bigger jar that contains two times more water than Joel's jar. What is the total volume of water in both jars?

   Hint: "two times more" does not mean "twice as much as."

10. A big container has 12 L of water. Given 2 pails of capacities 5 L and 9 L, how can you divide the volume of water equally between 2 of the containers?

    Hint: The aim is to get 6 L of water in each pail.

    Extension: What is the least number of steps needed to achieve this?

7 Money

Worked Example 1

Jeremy and Rita have $52.80 altogether. If Rita has $18.90, how much more money does Jeremy have than Rita?

$18.90

Rita
Jeremy

$52.80

?

$52.80 − $18.90 = $33.90

Jeremy has $33.90.

$33.90 − $18.90 = $15

Jeremy has **$15** more than Rita.

To check whether the answer is reasonable or sensible, do a quick mental calculation:

$52.80 is close to $53.

$18.90 is close to $19.

$53 − $19 = $54 − $20 = $34

$34 − $19 = $35 − $20 = $15 ✔

Worked Example 2

Mrs. Tan bought 9 muffins at 95¢ each. If she paid for the items with two $10 bills, how much change would she get?

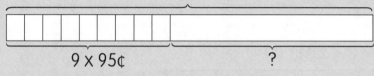

2 x $10 = $20

9 x 95¢   ?

9 × 95¢ = 855¢

855¢ = $8.55

9 muffins cost $8.55.

> 95 = 100 − 5
> 95 × 9 = 100 × 9 − 5 × 9
>   = 855

$20.00 − $8.55 = $11.45

She would get **$11.45** change.

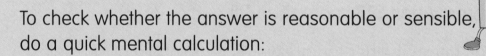

To check whether the answer is reasonable or sensible, do a quick mental calculation:

95¢ is close to $1.

9 × $1 = $9; 2 × $10 = $20

$20 − $9 = $11

So you expect the answer to be close to $11.

Worked Example 3

Joe and Ruth have $62.80 in total. Joe has $18.80 more than Ruth. How much money does each have?

Method 1

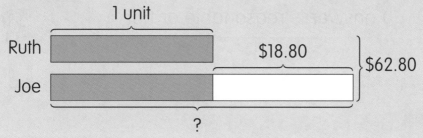

2 units = $62.80 − $18.80 = $44

1 unit = $44 ÷ 2 = $22 and $22 + $18.80 = $40.80

Ruth has **$22** and Joe has **$40.80**.

Method 2

Twice of Joe's money = $62.80 + $18.80
                     = $81.60

$81.60 ÷ 2 = $40.80
$40.80 − $18.80 = $22

Ruth has **$22** and Joe has **$40.80**.

Practice Questions

Answer all questions. Show your work and write your statements clearly.

1. Betty has $18.70, Cathy has $33.40, and Danny has $52.10. How much money do all three have in total?

> Estimate your answer mentally to check whether the computed answer is reasonable or not.

2. Matthew bought a shirt for $22.90 and a pair of pants for $42.50. He paid for both items with a $100 bill. How much change did he receive?

3. Kelvin and Jack shared $28 equally. If Jack donated $5.60 to charity, how much money did he have left?

4. After buying five coloring books that cost $3 each, Mary had $8.50 left. How much money did she have at first?

5. The total savings of Jenny and Irene are $51.35. If Jenny saves $23.80, how much more money does Irene save than Jenny?

6. Joshua plans to buy a basketball costing $27.35. His godfather gives him five $1 bills and two $10 bills. How much more money does he need?

7. Jim and Justin have the same amount of money at first. Jim receives $12.50 from his father while Justin gives $12.50 to his sister. How much more money does Jim have than Justin now?

8. Jennifer has $35. She plans to save $5 a week to buy a dress that costs $95. How many weeks must she save before she can buy the dress?

9. Roy and June have $137 altogether. June has $29 more than Roy. How much money does each have?

10. Tim had to mail the following packages:

    (a) Package 1 cost 42¢.

    (b) Package 2 cost 76¢.

    (c) Package 3 cost 94¢.

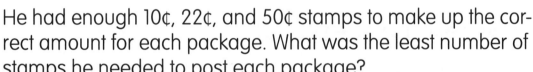

He had enough 10¢, 22¢, and 50¢ stamps to make up the correct amount for each package. What was the least number of stamps he needed to post each package?

Extension: What would be the most number of stamps he could use to post each package?

Challenging Problems

Worked Example 1

Chris buys some cookies at 20¢ each. He then sells them for 25¢ each. How many cookies must he sell in order to earn $1.20?

He made 25¢ – 20¢ = 5¢ on every cookie he sells.

Method 1

$1.20 = 120¢
120 ÷ 5 = 240 ÷ 10 = 24

Chris must sell **24** cookies.

Method 2

$1.20 = 120¢
120 ÷ 5 = ?
120 = 100 + 20
= 5 × 20 + 5 × 4
20 + 4 = 24

Chris must sell **24** cookies.

Worked Example 2

Samuel has four times as much money as Ben. If Samuel has $90 more than Ben, how much money do they have in all?

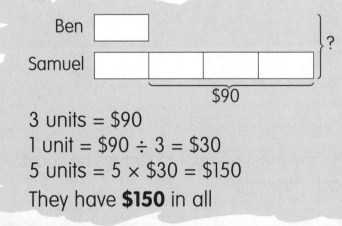

3 units = $90
1 unit = $90 ÷ 3 = $30
5 units = 5 × $30 = $150
They have **$150** in all

Worked Example 3

One mango and one pear cost $3.30. Two mangoes and five pears cost $9.00. How much does one mango cost?

Method 1

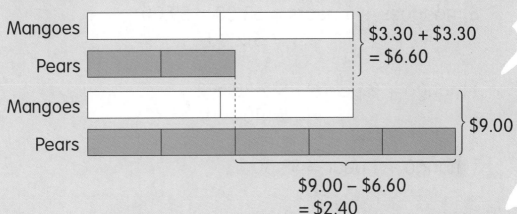

3 pears cost $2.40.

$2.40 = 240¢
240¢ ÷ 3 = 80¢
80¢ = $0.80

1 pear costs $0.80.
1 mango + $0.80 = $3.30
1 mango = $3.30 − $0.80
       = $2.50

One mango costs **$2.50**.

Check:
5 pears = 5 x $0.80
      = $4.00
2 mangoes + 5 pears
= $5.00 + $4.00 = $9.00

Method 2

1 mango + 1 pear = $3.30 (given)
2 mangoes + 5 pears = $9.00 (given)

3 mangoes + 6 pears = $3.30 + $9.00
= $12.30

1 mango + 2 pears = $12.30 ÷ 3
= $4.10

1 mango + 1 pear = $3.30

So, 1 pear = $4.10 − $3.30
= $0.80

1 mango = $3.30 − $0.80
= $2.50

One mango costs **$2.50**.

We make the number of mangoes equal so that it is easier to compare the pears.

Answer all questions. Show your work and write your statements clearly.

1. Jonathan buys some fish for 80¢ each. He then sells them for $1.20 each. How many fish must he sell in order to earn $4.80?

2. Smith has $12.40. Jane has $3.50 more than Smith but $4.65 less than Robin. How much money do Robin and Jane have altogether?

3. Mr. Tan sells apples at 40¢ each. Mr. Yang sells five apples for $1.80. If you are buying five apples, who should you buy from if you want to spend less money? Why?

4. Ashley has four times as much money as Dave. If Ashley has $180 more than Dave, how much money do they have in total?

5. A vending machine has yellow balls, green balls, and blue balls. Each ball costs $1. The balls fall into a bag you cannot see into. What is the least amount of money you need to spend to be sure there are 2 balls of the same color in the bag?

Extension: What would be the most amount you would need to spend to ensure that 3 balls are of the same color?

6. Anne has three times as much money as Eve. If Eve has $70 less than Anne, how much money do they have altogether?

7. In total, Adam and Pam have $58.10. Pam has $9.90 more than Adam. How much does each have?

8. A dealer pays $15.30 for 9 badges. He sells each badge for $2. How much profit does he make on each badge?

9. Henry bought two items. He paid with two $10 bills and got $2.40 change. Which items did he buy from the list below?

Item	Price
T-shirt	$7.90
Shorts	$9.50
Socks	$5.70
Jacket	$8.10
Shoes	$12.90

10. One pear and two oranges cost $1.00. Two pears and one orange cost $1.10. What is the total cost of two pears and two oranges?

 8 Fractions

Worked Example 1

How many more triangles must be shaded so that $\frac{3}{4}$ of the figure is shaded?

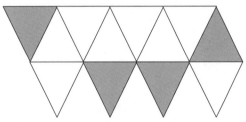

There are 12 triangles in the figure.

$$\frac{3}{4} = \frac{3 \times 3}{4 \times 3} = \frac{9}{12}$$

$\frac{3}{4}$ of the figure is made up of 9 triangles.

Only 4 triangles are shaded.

$9 - 4 = 5$

5 more triangles must be shaded so that $\frac{3}{4}$ of the figure is shaded.

Worked Example 2

Arrange the following fractions in order, beginning with the greatest.

$$\frac{1}{4} \quad \frac{1}{5} \quad \frac{7}{8} \quad \frac{1}{2}$$

Method 1

$$\frac{1}{4} = \frac{2}{8} \qquad \frac{1}{4} = \frac{5}{20}$$

$$\frac{1}{2} = \frac{4}{8} \qquad \frac{1}{5} = \frac{4}{20}$$

$\left.\right\}$ $\frac{1}{4}$ is greater than $\frac{1}{5}$

$$\frac{7}{8}$$

Beginning with the greatest, we have $\frac{7}{8}$, $\frac{1}{2}$, $\frac{1}{4}$, $\frac{1}{5}$.

Method 2

$\frac{1}{4}$

$\frac{1}{5}$

$\frac{7}{8}$

$\frac{1}{2}$

From the model, beginning with the greatest,
we have $\frac{7}{8}$, $\frac{1}{2}$, $\frac{1}{4}$, $\frac{1}{5}$.

Worked Example 3

Terrence cut a cake into 6 equal pieces and ate 2 pieces. Jane cut the remaining cake into 8 equal pieces and took 3 pieces. What fraction of the cake was left?

$\frac{4}{6}$ left $\qquad$ = $\qquad$ $\frac{8}{12}$ left

After Terrence cut the cake, the fraction of the cake left

$= \frac{4}{6} = \frac{8}{12}$

Each piece of the remaining cake represents $\frac{1}{12}$ of the cake.

Three pieces of the remaining cake represent $\frac{3}{12}$ of the cake.

After Jane took 3 pieces of cake, the fraction of the cake left

$= \frac{8}{12} - \frac{3}{12}$

$= \frac{5}{12}$

$\frac{5}{12}$ of the cake was left.

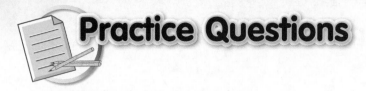

Practice Questions

Answer all questions. Show your work and write your statements clearly.

1. James had 12 marbles. He lost 3 of them. What fraction of the marbles was left? Express your answer in the simplest form.

2. Robert won 18 stuffed toys at a fair. He gave 6 stuffed toys to charity. What fraction of the stuffed toys was left? Express your answer in the simplest form.

3. How many quarters are there in 9 wholes?

4. The figure below is made up of 12 identical rectangles. What fraction of the figure is shaded?

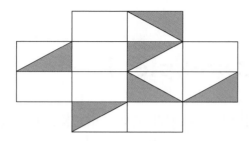

5. Given that $\frac{6}{9} = \frac{4}{\boxed{}}$, what number does $\boxed{}$ stand for?

6. Shade $\frac{3}{5}$ of the figure below.

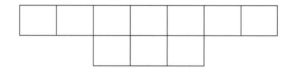

7. Arrange the following fractions in order, beginning with the smallest.

$$\frac{1}{2} \quad \frac{5}{6} \quad \frac{3}{4}$$

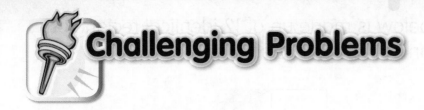

Challenging Problems

Worked Example 1

Joe used the following pattern blocks to make fraction sentences in (a) pictures, (b) words, (c) numbers.

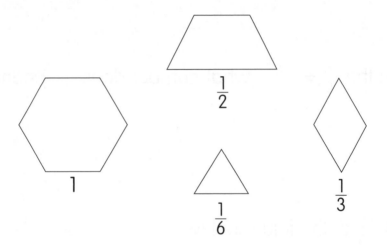

For example,

(a) 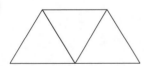 is the same as  .

(b) Three sixths is the same as one half.

(c) $\frac{3}{6} = \frac{1}{2}$

Using the pattern blocks, write all possible fraction sentences for the number 1 when using only one kind of block.

1. (a) 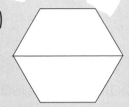 is the same as .

   (b) Two halves is the same as one whole.

   (c) $\frac{2}{2} = 1$

2. (a)  is the same as 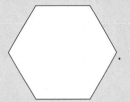.

   (b) Three thirds is the same as one whole.

   (c) $\frac{3}{3} = 1$

3. (a) 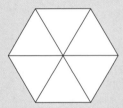 is the same as 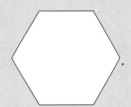.

   (b) Six sixths is the same as one whole.

   (c) $\frac{6}{6} = 1$

Worked Example 2

Sam gave $\frac{1}{7}$ of his stamps to Ann. He gave $\frac{1}{3}$ of what was left to Mary, and the remaining stamps to Susan.
(a) What fraction of Sam's stamps did Mary receive?
(b) What fraction of Sam's stamps did Susan receive?

Let the number of stamps Sam had be divided into 7 equal parts.

Ann

After Sam had given $\frac{1}{7}$ of his stamps to Ann, there were 6 parts left.

$\frac{1}{3} = \frac{2}{6}$

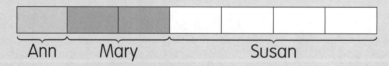

Ann   Mary   Susan

Out of 6 parts, Sam gave 2 parts to Mary and the remaining 4 parts to Susan.

(a) Mary received 2 out of 7 parts. Mary received $\frac{2}{7}$ of Sam's stamps.

(b) Susan received 4 out of 7 parts. Susan received $\frac{4}{7}$ of Sam's stamps.

Answer all questions. Show your work and write your statements clearly.

1. Using as many of the pattern blocks below as needed, form fraction sentences for equivalent fractions in (a) pictures, (b) words, (c) numbers. Use only one kind of block for each sentence.

   Hint: See Worked Example 1.

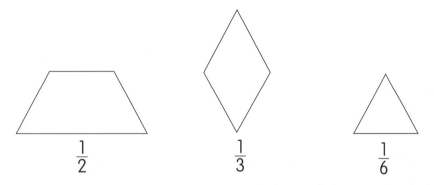

$\frac{1}{2}$ $\frac{1}{3}$ $\frac{1}{6}$

2. Study the figures below, and fill in the missing numbers.

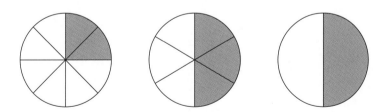

(a) $\dfrac{1}{\square} + \dfrac{1}{\square} = \dfrac{1}{4}$

(b) $\dfrac{1}{\square} + \dfrac{1}{\square} + \dfrac{1}{\square} = \dfrac{1}{2}$

3. If 18 represents half of the circle below, what number is represented by the shaded part of the circle?

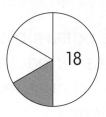

4. Study the figures below. Fill in the missing numbers given that they are the same.

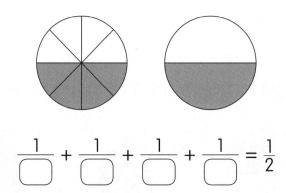

$$\frac{1}{\bigcirc} + \frac{1}{\bigcirc} + \frac{1}{\bigcirc} + \frac{1}{\bigcirc} = \frac{1}{2}$$

5. (a) With the help of the diagram below, find a pair of fractions whose sum is $\frac{7}{10}$.

(b) With the help of the diagram below, find a pair of fractions such that one fraction is $\frac{3}{10}$ more than the other.

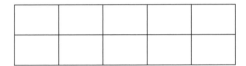

6. Richard painted $\frac{1}{5}$ of a rod blue and $\frac{1}{4}$ of the remainder green. What fraction of the rod was not painted?

Hint: Draw a model.

7. Mrs. Yan had one meter of string. She used $\frac{5}{10}$ m of the string to tie a box and another $\frac{3}{10}$ m to make a pendulum. What length of string was left?

8. Oliver gave $\frac{1}{9}$ of his stickers to Mark. He then gave $\frac{1}{4}$ of the remaining stickers to Paul, and the rest to Karen.
    (a) What fraction of Oliver's stickers were given to Paul?
    (b) What fraction of Oliver's stickers were given to Karen?

9 Time

Worked Example 1

How many minutes are there between 10:35 P.M. on Saturday and 1:27 A.M. the next day?

Method 1

10:35 P.M. $\xrightarrow{\text{2 h}}$ 12:35 A.M. $\xrightarrow{\text{25 min}}$ 1:00 A.M.

$\downarrow$ 27 min

1:27 A.M.

2 h = 2 × 60
= 120 min

120 min + 25 min + 27 min = 172 min

There are **172** minutes between 10:35 P.M. on Saturday and 1:27 A.M. the next day.

Method 2

From 10:27 P.M. to 10:35 P.M., there are 8 minutes.
From 10:27 P.M. to 1:27 A.M., there are 3 hours,
or 3 × 60 = 180 minutes.

180 − 8 = 172

So, there are **172** minutes between the two times.

Worked Example 2

Ivan took 1 h 32 min to learn how to fold a paper rat. He took 47 min more to learn how to fold a paper rabbit than that taken to fold the paper rat. How long did he take to learn how to fold the paper rat and paper rabbit?

1 h 32 min

Paper rat

Paper rabbit

?

47 min

Method 1

1 h 32 min + 47 min = 1 h 79 min
= 2 h 19 min

Ivan took 2 h 19 min to learn how to fold the paper rabbit.

1 h 32 min + 2 h 19 min = 3 h 51 min

He took **3 h 51 min** to learn how to fold the paper rat and paper rabbit.

Method 2

2 × 1 h 32 min = 2 h 64 min
= 3 h 4 min
3 h 4 min + 47 min = 3 h 51 min

He took **3 h 51 min** to learn how to fold the paper rat and paper rabbit.

Worked Example 3

Jeremy took 7 h 20 min to work out ten challenging problems. Rashid solved the same problems 45 minutes faster than Jeremy. Both of them started working on the problems at 1:30 P.M.
(a) How long did Rashid take to solve all ten problems?
(b) At what time did Rashid finish solving the problems?

(a) 45 min = 20 min + 25 min

$$7 \text{ h } 20 \text{ min } \xrightarrow{-20 \text{ min}} 7 \text{ h } \xrightarrow{-25 \text{ min}} 6 \text{ h } 35 \text{ min}$$

Rashid took **6 h 35 min** to solve all ten problems.

(b)

$$1:30 \text{ P.M. } \xrightarrow{+6 \text{ h}} 7:30 \text{ P.M. } \xrightarrow{+35 \text{ min}} 8:05 \text{ P.M.}$$

Rashid finished solving the problems at **8:05 P.M.**

Practice Questions

Answer all questions. Show your work and write your statements clearly.

1. A movie started at 8:15 P.M. and ended at 10:00 P.M. How long did the movie last?

2. Mrs. Aguilar began her lesson at 11:35 A.M. and finished at 12:15 P.M. How long was she teaching?

3. An amusement park is open from 8:30 A.M. to 6:00 P.M. every day except on Sundays. How long is the amusement park open each day?

4. A movie ended at 8:15 P.M. It lasted for 80 minutes. At what time did the movie start?

5. Yesterday was Monday. What day is 4 days after tomorrow?

6. How many minutes are there between 9:40 P.M. on Sunday and 2:15 A.M. the next day?

7. Henry took 1 h 26 min to build a toy castle. He took 32 min more to build a toy castle than to build a toy house. How long did he take to build a toy castle and a toy house altogether?

8. Jennifer and Ian spent a total of 32 minutes jogging around their neighborhood. Jennifer took 4 minutes more than Ian. How long did Jennifer jog?

9. How many days are there from May 18 to June 17?

Challenging Problems

Worked Example 1

Bus service 28 leaves the terminal every 10 minutes.
Bus service 111 leaves the same terminal every 15 minutes.
On Sunday, both bus services leave the terminal at 9:00 A.M.
When will both bus services next leave the terminal together?

Method 1

Time of departure	
Bus service 28	**Bus service 111**
9:00 A.M.	9:00 A.M.
9:10 A.M.	9:15 A.M.
9:20 A.M.	9:30 A.M.
9:30 A.M.	9:45 A.M.

Both bus services will next leave the terminal together
at **9:30 A.M.**

Method 2

Bus 28 leaves after	Bus 111 leaves after
10 min	15 min
20 min	**30 min**
30 min	45 min

9:00 A.M. $\xrightarrow{\text{+ 30 min}}$ 9:30 A.M.

Both bus services will next leave the terminal together
at **9:30 A.M.**

Worked Example 2

A train service runs every 15 minutes. If there is a train at 7:25 A.M., how many trains are there between 6:00 A.M. and 9:00 A.M. altogether?

Time	
6:10 A.M.	7:40 A.M.
6:25 A.M.	7:55 A.M.
6:40 A.M.	8:10 A.M.
6:55 A.M.	8:25 A.M.
7:10 A.M.	8:40 A.M.
7:25 A.M.	8:55 A.M.

We take note of all the times before and after 7:25 A.M. at 15-minute intervals between 6:00 A.M. and 9:00 A.M.

There are **12** trains between 6:00 A.M. and 9:00 A.M. altogether.

For example,

$$7:25 \text{ A.M.} \xrightarrow{-15 \text{ min}} 7:10 \text{ A.M.}$$

$$7:25 \text{ A.M.} \xrightarrow{+15 \text{ min}} 7:40 \text{ A.M.}$$

From the table, there are 12 different times.

Worked Example 3

Yesterday was Tuesday. What day is 3 days before 4 days after tomorrow?

Step 1: Yesterday was Tuesday.

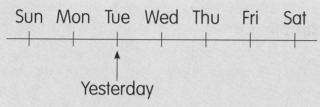

Yesterday

Step 2: Today is Wednesday.

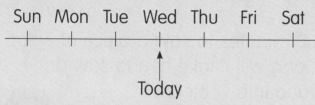

Today

Step 3: Tomorrow is Thursday.

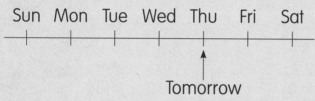

Tomorrow

Step 4: 4 days after tomorrow.

Tomorrow   4 days after tomorrow

Step 5: 3 days before 4 days after tomorrow.

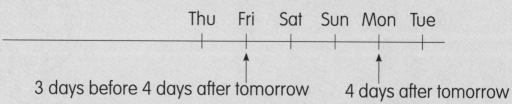

3 days before 4 days after tomorrow   4 days after tomorrow

3 days before 4 days after tomorrow is a **Friday**.

Answer all questions. Show your work and write your statements clearly.

1. Tomorrow is Sunday. What day is 3 days after 3 days before yesterday?

    Hint: See Worked Example 3.

2. A carpenter takes 60 minutes to saw a piece of wood into 6 pieces. How long will it take him to saw an identical piece of wood into 11 pieces?

3. A clock loses 5 minutes every hour. The clock is adjusted to the correct time at 8:00 A.M. on Sunday. What time will it show at 8:00 A.M. on the following Monday?

4. (a) On what dates of a month is the sum of the digits equal to 4?
   (b) What is the least and most number of times these dates will occur in a month?

5. A bus service runs every 15 minutes. If there is a bus at 9:20 A.M., how many buses are there between 8:00 A.M. and 11:00 A.M. altogether?

   Hint: See Worked Example 2.

6. Tom has a habit of adjusting his watch every hour, by making it run 5 minutes faster than usual. If he first adjusts his watch at 5 P.M., what is the correct time when his watch shows 9 P.M.?

7. Sally is 12 years old. The digits of her age can be
    switched to obtain her cousin's age. In the near future,
    their ages can be obtained by switching the digits of
    their ages again. In how many years' time will this
    happen again?

    Hint: Draw a table and find their ages each year.

8. How many minutes are there between 9:25 P.M.
    on Wednesday and 1:19 A.M. on Friday?

9. Perry and Celeste took a total of 14 minutes 26 seconds
    to cycle around a few apartments. Perry took 3 minutes
    38 seconds less than Celeste. How long (in minutes and
    seconds) did Celeste cycle?

    Hint: 1 minute = 60 seconds

10. The clocks show the times in three cities at the same time.

| Geneva | Singapore | Sydney |
| Sun, 6:30 A.M. | Sun, 1:30 P.M. | Sun, 4:30 P.M. |

(a) What is the time difference between Geneva and Singapore?

(b) What is the time difference between Singapore and Sydney?

(c) If it is 6:10 A.M. in Singapore, what is the time in Geneva?

(d) If it is 10:25 A.M. in Sydney, what is the time in Singapore?

10 Data Analysis

Worked Example 1

The bar graph below shows the number of animals sold by a pet shop in one month.

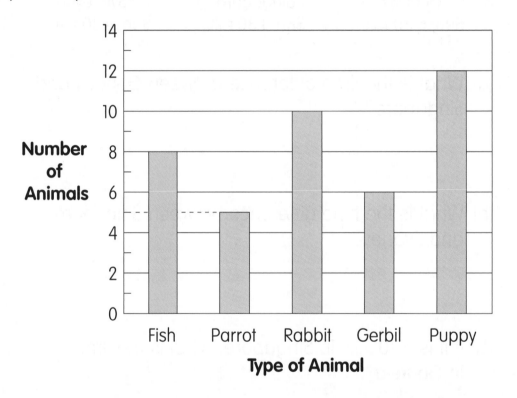

(a) How many parrots were sold during the month?

(b) How many more puppies than fishes were sold?

(c) How many fewer gerbils than rabbits were sold?

(a)

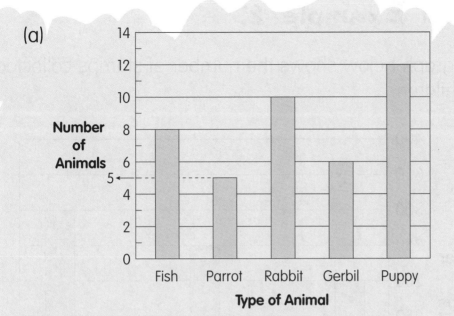

The height of the bar representing "Parrots" is 5 units. This means that **5** parrots were sold during the month.

(b) The bar graph shows that 8 fishes and 12 puppies were sold during the month.

$12 - 8 = 4$

4 more puppies than fishes were sold.

(c) The bar graph shows that 6 gerbils and 10 rabbits were sold.

$10 - 6 = 4$

4 fewer gerbils than rabbits were sold.

Worked Example 2

The bar graph below shows the number of stamps collected by five children.

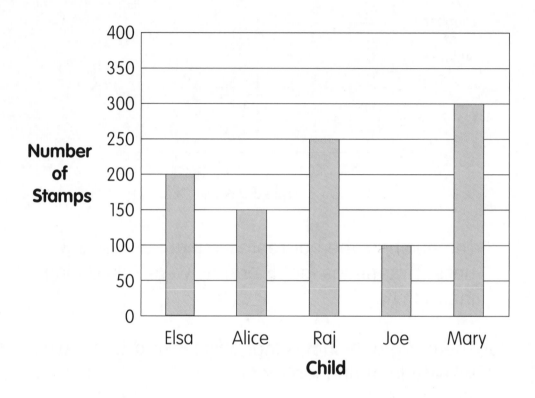

(a) How many more stamps does Raj have than Joe?

(b) How many fewer stamps does Alice have than Mary?

(c) How many stamps do Elsa, Mary, and Raj have altogether?

(a) The bar graph shows that Raj has 250 stamps and Joe has 100 stamps.

$250 - 100 = 150$

Raj has **150** more stamps than Joe.

(b) The bar graph shows that Alice has 150 stamps and Mary has 300 stamps.

$300 - 150 = 150$

Alice has **150** fewer stamps than Mary.

(c) Elsa has 200 stamps, Mary has 300 stamps, and Raj has 250 stamps.

$200 + 300 + 250 = 750$

Elsa, Mary, and Raj have **750** stamps altogether.

Worked Example 3

The bar graph below shows the number of computers sold by a computer shop in a week.

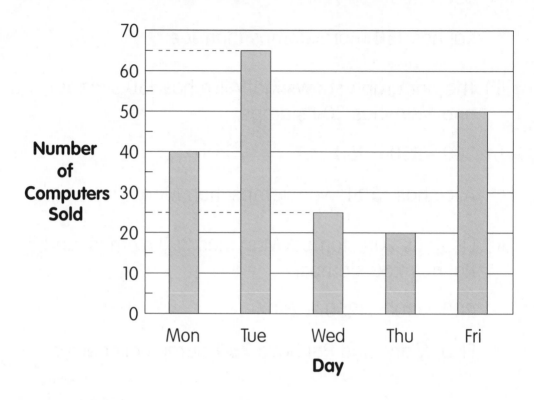

(a) How many more computers were sold on Tuesday than on Thursday?

(b) How many fewer computers were sold on Wednesday than on Monday?

(c) How many computers were sold during the week?

(a) The bar graph shows that the shop sold 65 computers on Tuesday and 20 computers on Thursday.

65 − 20 = 45

45 more computers were sold on Tuesday than on Thursday.

(b) The bar graph shows that the shop sold 40 computers on Monday and 25 computers on Wednesday.

40 − 25 = 15

15 fewer computers were sold on Wednesday than on Monday.

(c)

Day	Number of computers sold
Monday	40
Tuesday	65
Wednesday	25
Thursday	20
Friday	50

40 + 65 + 25 + 20 + 50 = 200

200 computers were sold during the week.

Worked Example 4

The following line plot shows the number of games apps a group of boys and girls recently played on their parents' smartphones.

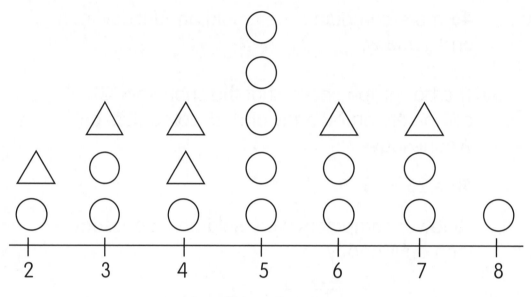

Number of games

Key: ◯ Boys

△ Girls

(a) How many boys and girls were there altogether?
(b) What is the most common number of apps the children played?
(c) How many boys played fewer than 5 games?
(d) How many girls played more than 4 games?
(e) What fraction of the girls played fewer than 7 games?
(f) How many more boys played 5 games than 8 games?

(a) The total number of ◯s and △s is 20.
There were **20** boys and girls altogether.

(b) The line plot shows that most number of children played 5 game apps.
Therefore, the most common number of apps the children played is **5**.

(c) We look for the number of ◯s in columns 2, 3, and 4.

There are 4 ◯s in total.
4 boys played fewer than 5 games.

(d) In columns 5, 6, 7, and 8, there are only 2 △s.
2 girls played more than 4 games.

(e) From columns 2 to 6, there are 5 △s.

Now, $\dfrac{\text{number of girls}}{\text{number of children}} = \dfrac{5}{20} = \dfrac{1}{4}$

$\dfrac{1}{4}$ of the girls played fewer than 7 games.

(f) 5 boys played 5 games.
1 boy played 8 games.
$5 - 1 = 4$

There are **4** more boys who played 5 games than 8 games.

Practice Questions

Answer all questions. Show your work and write your statements clearly.

1. The bar graph below shows subjects: history, math, English, or science that students liked best.

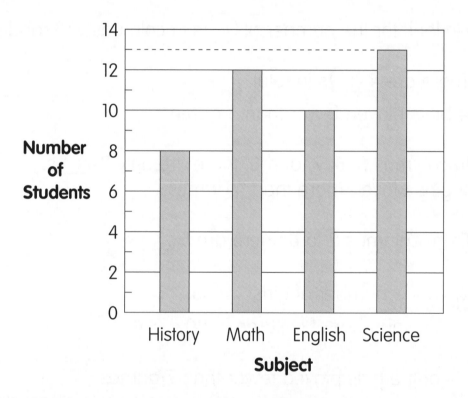

(a) Which is the most popular subject?
(b) How many more students prefer English to History?
(c) What is the total number of students in the class?

2. A group of students were asked to name their favorite color among the choices of purple, red, blue, and green only.

The total number of students who liked red, blue, and green was five times as many as those who liked purple.

Complete the bar graph below.

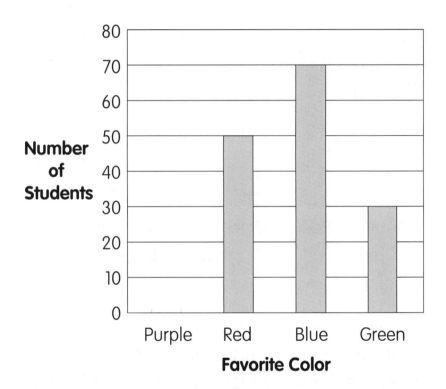

3. A group of students were asked to choose which of 5 colors they liked best. The bar graph below summarizes the results.

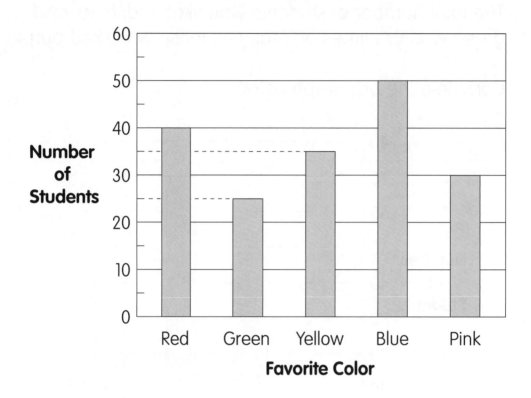

(a) How many students liked yellow?
(b) What was the most popular color?
(c) How many more students preferred red to pink?

4. A group of adults were asked to name their preferred mode of transport. The bar graph below shows the results.

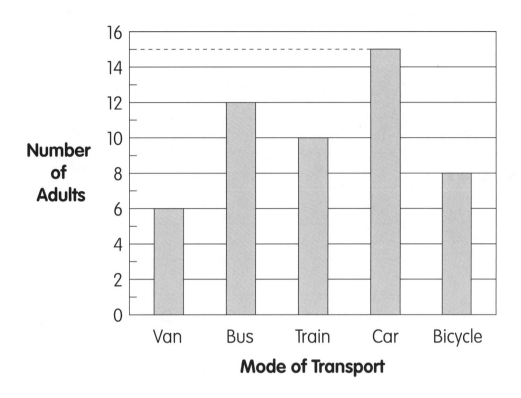

(a) How many adults preferred to travel by bus, car, or van in all?

(b) There were as many adults who traveled by van and by bus as those who traveled by _____ and by _____.

(c) How many more adults traveled by car than by bicycle?

(d) What is the difference between the number of adults who chose the most popular and the least popular mode of transport?

5. The bar graph below shows the hobbies of some teenagers in a town.

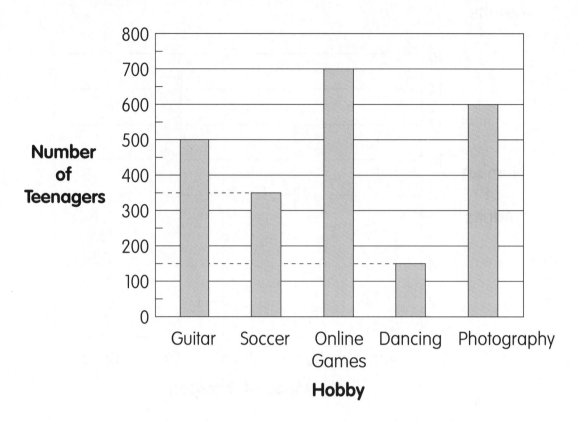

(a) What is the most popular hobby?
(b) How many teenagers like to play guitar?
(c) How many more teenagers prefer photography to dancing?
(d) How many teenagers like soccer or dancing altogether?
(e) How many fewer teenagers like dancing than online games?

6. The following table shows the mass of some students measured to the nearest kilogram.

40	43	45	35	42	43
45	50	37	38	41	39
41	49	32	40	43	43

(a) Draw a line plot to show the data.
(b) How many of the students were between 38 kg and 42 kg?
(c) How many students were heavier than 40 kg?
(d) How many students were lighter than 38 kg?
(e) What was the most common mass?

7. Mr. Yan gave a math quiz to a group of 14 students. He drew this line plot to show which questions the students got wrong most often.

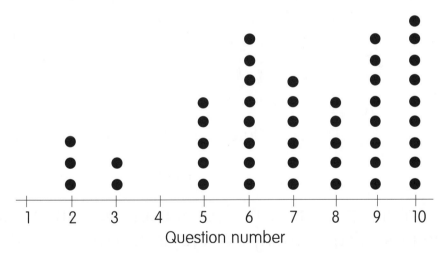

Question number

(a) How many questions were on the quiz?
(b) Which questions did all students answer correctly?
(c) Which question was the most difficult for most students?
(d) What fraction of the students got question 9 wrong?
(e) What fraction of the students got question 7 correct?

Worked Example 1

The bar graph below shows the number of stickers collected by five children.

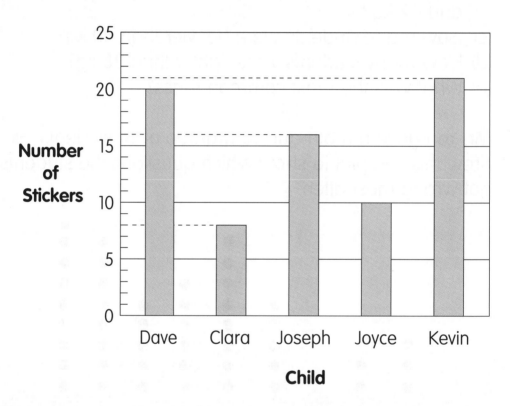

(a) How many more stickers does Joseph have than Clara?

(b) Who has twice as many stickers as Joyce?

(c) Who has half as many stickers as Joseph?

(d) What is the difference between the most number of stickers collected and the least number of stickers collected?

(e) All five children decide to share their stickers equally. How many stickers will each have after sharing?

(a) The bar graph shows that Joseph has 16 stickers and Clara has 8 stickers.

16 – 8 = 8

Joseph has **8** more stickers than Clara.

(b) The bar graph shows that Joyce has 10 stickers.

2 × 10 = 20

From the bar graph, Dave has 20 stickers.

Dave has twice as many stickers as Joyce.

(c) The bar graph shows that Joseph has 16 stickers and Clara has 8 stickers.

16 ÷ 2 = 8

Clara has half as many stickers as Joseph.

(d) The bar graph shows that Kevin has the most number of stickers (21) and Clara has the least number of stickers (8).

21 – 8 = 13

The difference in the number of stickers collected is **13**.

(e)

Child	Number of stickers
Dave	20
Clara	8
Joseph	16
Joyce	10
Kevin	21

20 + 8 + 16 + 10 + 21 = 75

75 ÷ 5 = 15

Each child will have **15** stickers after sharing.

Worked Example 2

A survey was carried out to find out the flavor of ice cream among 5 choices that children like most. The bar graph below summarizes the results.

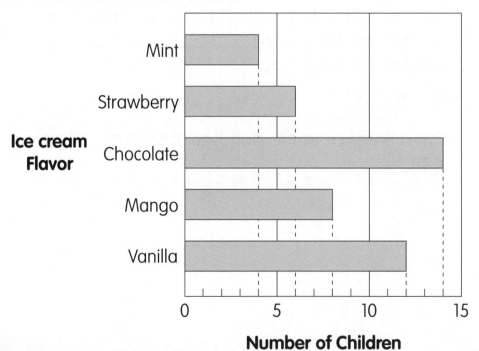

(a) How many children liked chocolate ice cream most?

(b) Which ice cream flavor was the least popular?

(c) Which ice cream flavor was twice as popular as strawberry flavor?

(d) How many fewer children preferred mango to vanilla ice cream?

(e) How many children took part in the survey?

(a)

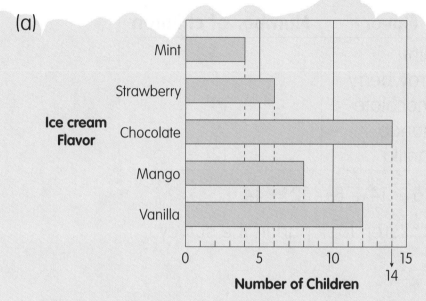

14 children liked chocolate ice cream most.

(b) The shortest bar in the graph represent mint ice cream.

Mint ice cream was the least popular.

(c) The bar graph show that 6 children liked strawberry ice cream.

$2 \times 6 = 12$

The bar graph show that 12 children liked vanilla ice cream.

Vanilla ice cream was twice as popular as strawberry ice cream.

(d) The bar graph show that 8 children liked mango ice cream and 12 children liked vanilla ice cream.

$12 - 8 = 4$

4 fewer children preferred mango to vanilla ice cream.

(e)

Flavor	Number of children
Mint	4
Strawberry	6
Chocolate	14
Mango	8
Vanilla	12

$4 + 6 + 14 + 8 + 12 = 44$

44 children took part in the survey.

Answer all questions. Show your work and write your statements clearly.

1. The bar graph below shows the number of souvenirs distributed by a mathematics society in a week during its annual event.

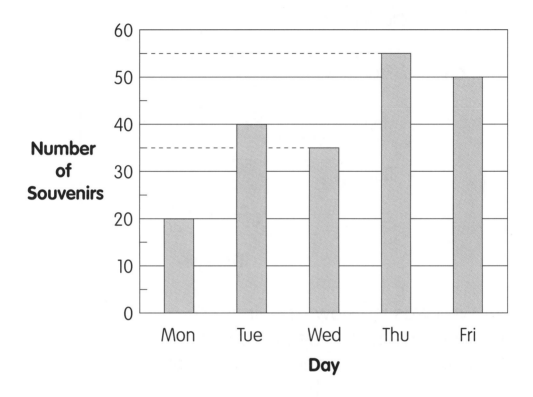

(a) How many souvenirs were distributed from Tuesday to Thursday?

(b) At the end of Friday, there were 15 souvenirs left. How many souvenirs did the mathematics society prepare for the week?

2. The bar graph below shows the times taken by five children to swim 50 meters.

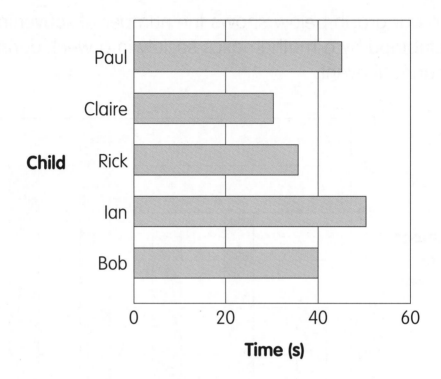

(a) Who was the slowest swimmer?
(b) Who was the fastest swimmer?
(c) Who was the second last swimmer?
(d) Who came in third?

Hint: The slowest/fastest swimmer takes more/less time.

3. Arthur collects stamps from countries in Southeast Asia. He has 15 Brunei stamps and twice as many Thailand stamps. He has 10 fewer Vietnam stamps than Thailand stamps. He has 20 more Malaysia stamps than Thailand stamps.

(a) Use the above information to complete the bar graph below.

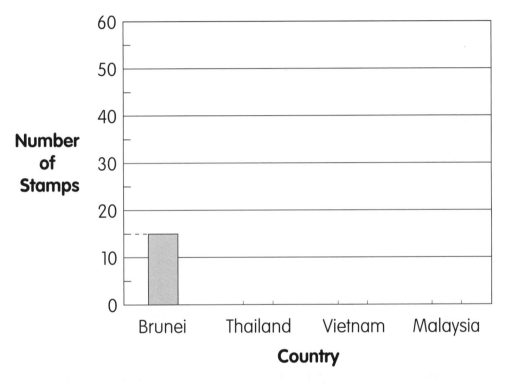

(b) Use the bar graph to answer these questions.

(i) Arthur has the most number of _____ stamps.

(ii) He has the least number of _____ stamps.

(iii) Arthur has _____ more Malaysia stamps than Brunei stamps.

(iv) Arthur has _____ stamps altogether.

4. Ally is 11 years old.
   Cathy is 3 years younger than Ally.
   Helen is 5 years older than Cathy.
   Joanne is 3 years younger than Helen.

   (a) Use the above information to complete the bar graph below.

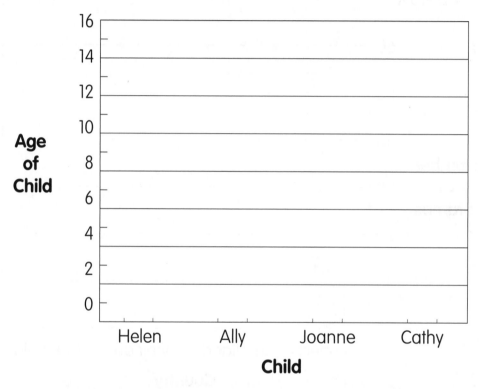

   (b) Use the bar graph to answer the following questions.
       (i)   What is the total age of Helen and Cathy?
       (ii) When Joanne reaches Helen's age, how old will Ally be?
       (iii) When Cathy reaches Joanne's age, how old will Helen be?

5. Aaron, Bob, Claire, and Dave sold a total of 1,000 concert tickets. Claire sold as many tickets as the total number of tickets sold by Aaron and Bob. Aaron sold half as many tickets as Bob. Dave sold twice as many tickets as Bob.

(a) Use the above information to complete the bar graph below.

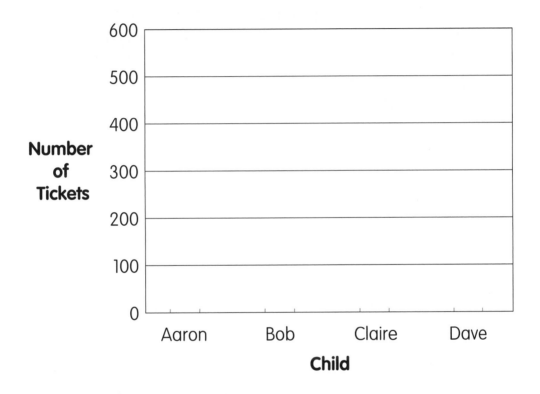

(b) Use the bar graph to answer these questions.
(i) Who sold the least number of tickets?
(ii) Who sold the most number of tickets?
(iii) How many more tickets would Bob have to sell in order to match the number of tickets sold by Claire?

11 Geometry

Worked Example 1

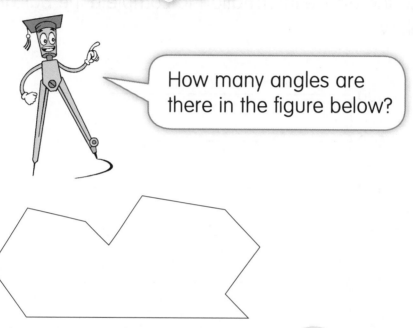

How many angles are there in the figure below?

In closed figures, only consider the internal angles.

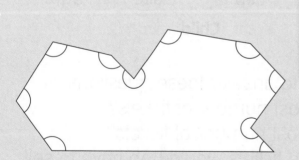

There are **10** angles.

Worked Example 2

How many right angles are there in the figure below?

Only consider inside angles.

There are **6** right angles.

Worked Example 3

Look at the figure below. How many angles are smaller than a right angle?

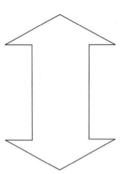

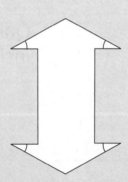

4 angles are smaller than a right angle.

Answer all questions. Show your work and write your statements clearly.

1. How many right angles are there in the figure below?

2. In the figure below, find the number of angles that are
   (a) smaller than a right angle,
   (b) greater than a right angle.

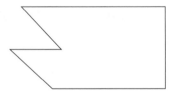

3. Study these angles and complete the table below.

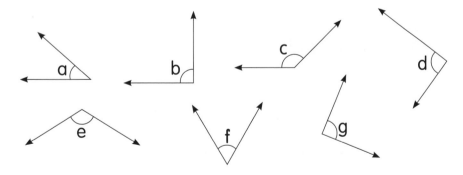

	Angle
Right angle	
Smaller than a right angle	
Greater than a right angle	

4. Look at the figure below.

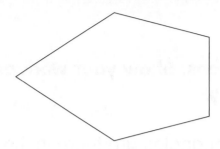

    (a) How many angles are right angles?
    (b) How many angles are smaller than a right angle?
    (c) How many angles are greater than a right angle?

5. Mark the angles that are smaller than a right angle.

6. Look at the figure below.

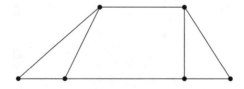

    (a) How many angles are right angles?
    (b) How many angles are smaller than a right angle?

Challenging Problems

Worked Example 1

Which angle measure is bigger?

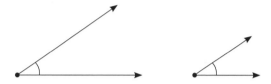

Both angle measures are the **same**, although the left angle measure appears to be bigger than the right angle measure due to the lengths of the lines that form their angles.

Worked Example 2

In the figure below, how many right angles are there?

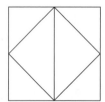

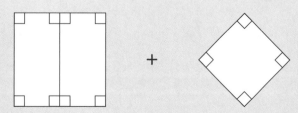

8 + 4 = 12

There are **12** right angles.

Answer all questions. Show your work and write your statements clearly.

1. Study the figures below and answer the following questions.

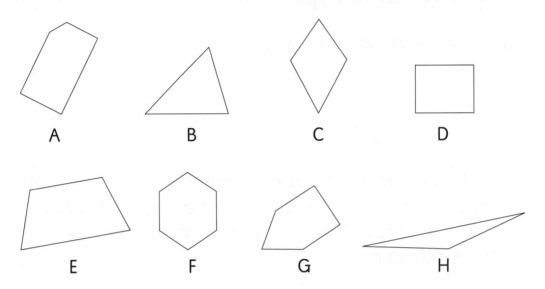

(a) Name two figures that have at least one right angle each.

(b) Name three figures that have at least one angle greater than a right angle.

(c) Name a figure with each of its angles smaller than a right angle.

(d) Name a figure with each of its angles greater than a right angle.

2. Which angle measure is smaller?

3. Look at the figure below. How many angle measure inside the figure are greater than a right angle?

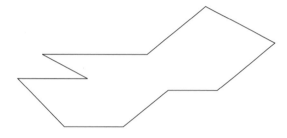

4. What is the greatest number of right angles that a six-sided figure can have? (A six-sided figure is a figure with 6 sides.)

5. In each of the following diagrams, how many right angles are there?

(a)

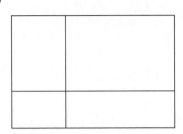

(b)

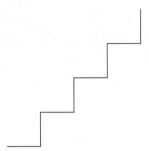

6. How many angle measures smaller than a right angle can be formed from this figure?

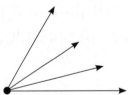

7. (a) Draw an angle with a measure that is greater than a right angle.
   (b) Draw an angle with a measure that is smaller than a right angle.

8. Fold a paper circle in half and then in half again. What fraction of a turn is a right angle?

12 Area and Perimeter

Worked Example 1

The figure shows a rectangular farm land. What is its perimeter? What is its area?

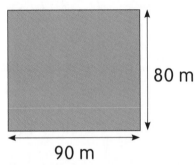

80 m

90 m

Perimeter = length + width + length + width
= 90 m + 80 m + 90 m + 80 m
= 340 m

Its perimeter is **340 m**.

Area = length × width
= 90 m × 80 m
= 7,200 m^2

Its area is **7,200 m^2**.

Another way to find perimeter is:
90 + 80 = 170
2 × 170 = 340

Worked Example 2

A rectangular painting is twice as long as it is wide. It is 60 cm long. What is its perimeter?

60 cm

Length

Width

60 cm ÷ 2 = 30 cm

Its width is 30 cm.

Perimeter = length + width + length + width
= 60 cm + 30 cm + 60 cm + 30 cm
= 180 cm

Its perimeter is **180 cm**.

Drawing a model helps us to visualize the situation better.

Extension: The area of a rectangle is 1,800 cm². Its length is twice its width. What is the perimeter of the rectangle?

Worked Example 3

What is the perimeter and area of each figure?

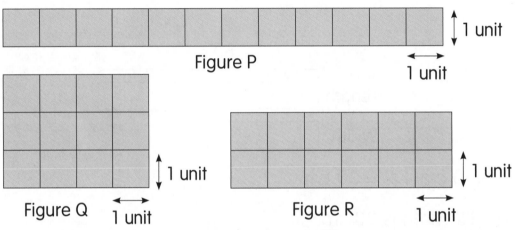

Figure P

1 unit

1 unit

Figure Q

1 unit

1 unit

Figure R

1 unit

1 unit

Perimeter of figure P = **26 units**
Perimeter of figure Q = **14 units**
Perimeter of figure R = **16 units**

The area of one square is 1 square unit.

By counting the squares in each figure,

area of figure P = **12 square units**
area of figure Q = **12 square units**
area of figure R = **12 square units**

The figures above have the same area but different perimeters.

Practice Questions

Answer all questions. Show your work and write your statements clearly.

1. The figure below shows a rectangular strip of paper. Find its area and perimeter.

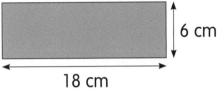

6 cm

18 cm

2. The figure shows a rectangular enclosure. Find the area and perimeter of the enclosure. How much does it cost to fence it if one meter of fencing costs $9?

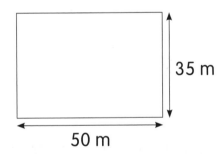

35 m

50 m

3. Henry ran around a rectangular field of length 175 m and width 80 m three times. Find the total distance that he ran.

4. A rectangular piece of cardboard is 3 times as long as it is wide. If it is 25 cm wide, find its perimeter.

5. What is the perimeter of this figure?

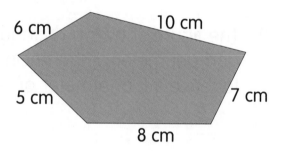

6. A wire is used to form a rectangle of length 12 cm and width 9 cm. What is the length of the wire?

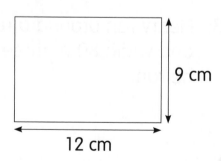

7. A wire of length 75 cm was used to form a square.
   If 3 cm of it was not used, find the length of the square.

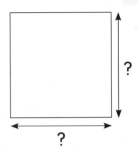

8. Each square in the following figures has an area of
   1 square unit. Find the area and perimeter of each figure.
   What is common among these figures?

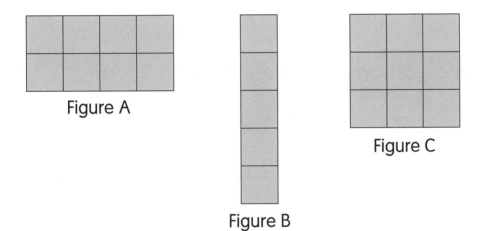

Figure A

Figure B

Figure C

Challenging Problems

Worked Example 1

Square ABCD is formed by 9 small squares. The perimeter of each small square is 8 cm. Find the perimeter of square ABCD.

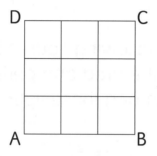

Length of each small square = 8 cm ÷ 4 = 2 cm

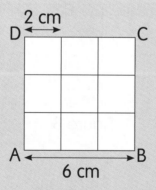

Length of square ABCD = 3 × 2 cm = 6 cm

Perimeter of square ABCD = 4 × 6 cm = 24 cm

The perimeter of square ABCD is **24 cm**.

Worked Example 2

What is the perimeter of the figure below?

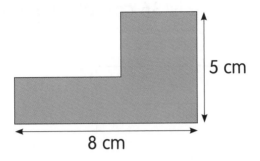

5 cm

8 cm

Shift the lines, as shown by the arrows.
They form a rectangle of length 8 cm and width 5 cm.

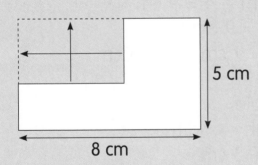

5 cm

8 cm

The given figure and the rectangle have the same perimeter.

Perimeter = length + width + length + width
= 8 cm + 5 cm + 8 cm + 5 cm
= 26 cm

The perimeter of the figure is **26 cm**.

Worked Example 3

The square is made up of 3 identical rectangles. The perimeter of the square is 36 cm. What is the perimeter of each rectangle?

Perimeter of square = 36 cm
Length of square = 36 cm ÷ 4 = 9 cm
Length of one rectangle = 9 cm
Width of one rectangle = 9 cm ÷ 3 = 3 cm

Perimeter of one rectangle
= length + width + length + width
= 9 cm + 3 cm + 9 cm + 3 cm
= 24 cm

The perimeter of each rectangle is **24 cm**.

Answer all questions. Show your work and write your statements clearly.

1. Find the perimeter and area of each of the following figures.

(a)

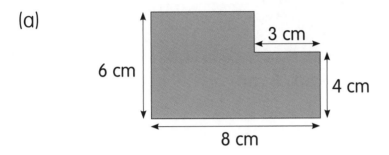

(b)

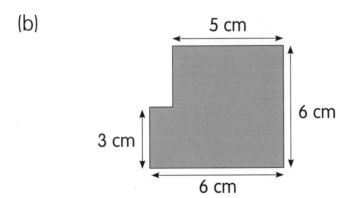

2. Find the perimeter of each of the following figures.

(a)

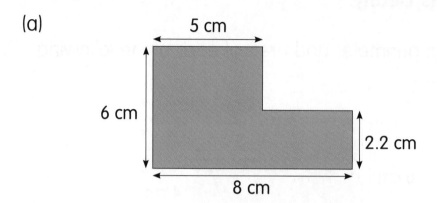

5 cm

6 cm

2.2 cm

8 cm

(b)

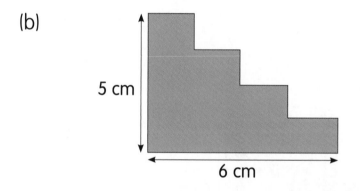

5 cm

6 cm

3. A square of side 12 cm has 4 of its corners cut off. What is the perimeter of the new figure?

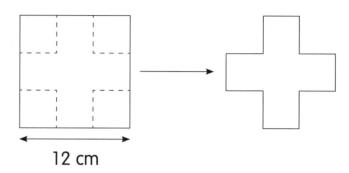

12 cm

4. Farmer Oates has an orchard 24 m long and 24 m wide. His orange trees are planted 8 m apart along the perimeter of the orchard. If each tree produces about 100 oranges, how many oranges can he expect to get from his orchard?

Hint: Draw a diagram to visualize the situation.

5. The figure consists of 5 squares, each of side 6 cm. What is the perimeter of the figure?

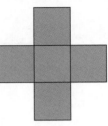

6. The square is made up of 3 identical rectangles. The perimeter of each rectangle is 16 cm. What is the perimeter of the square?

13 Review Questions 1

Worked Example 1

A container has a capacity of 3 liters. 1 L 50 mL of water is poured into it. How much more water must be added to fill the container completely?

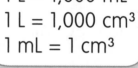

1 L = 1,000 mL
1 L = 1,000 cm³
1 mL = 1 cm³

3 L – 1 L 50 mL
= 1 L + 2 L – 1 L 50 mL
= 1 L + 1 L 1,000 mL – 1 L 50 mL
= 1 L + 950 mL
= 1 L 950 mL

1 L 950 mL of water must be added to fill the container.

Worked Example 2

Sally began her lesson at 4:05 P.M. However, the lesson took 30 minutes longer than usual and ended at 6:25 P.M. How long did the lesson usually last?

Method 1

$$4:05 \text{ P.M.} \xrightarrow{\text{2 h}} 6:05 \text{ P.M.} \xrightarrow{\text{20 min}} 6:25 \text{ P.M.}$$

From 4:05 P.M. to 6:25 P.M., there are 2 h 20 min.

$$2 \text{ h } 20 \text{ min} - 30 \text{ min} = \underbrace{2 \text{ h } 20 \text{ min} - 20 \text{ min}}_{\text{2 h}} - 10 \text{ min}$$
$$= 1 \text{ h } 50 \text{ min}$$

The lesson usually lasted **1 h 50 min**.

Method 2

$4:05$ P.M. $+ 30$ min $= 4:35$ P.M.

$$4:35 \text{ P.M.} \xrightarrow{\text{25 min}} 5:00 \text{ P.M.} \xrightarrow{\text{1 h 25 min}} 6:25 \text{ P.M.}$$

25 min + 1 h 25 min = 1 h 50 min

The lesson usually lasted was **1 h 50 min** long.

Practice Questions

Answer all questions. Show your work and write your statements clearly.

1. A large jug full of water can fill 2 small jugs. A small jug full of water can fill 5 cups. How many cups can be filled by a large jug full of water?

2. A jewelry shop opens at 10:00 A.M. every day and closes at 9:30 P.M. How long is the shop open each day?

3. (a) What is the largest three-digit number?
   (b) What is the smallest four-digit number?

4. Yvonne rented 5 DVDs. The rental charge for each DVD was the same. If she paid $2.50 for postage and her total bill was $17.50, find the rental charge for one DVD.

5. Write down the next three terms in the number sequence below.

   8, 13, 11, 16, 14, _____, _____, _____

6. I am thinking of a three-digit odd number. The three digits add up to 10. The tens digit is twice the hundreds digit. There are no zeros. What number am I thinking of?

7. A wire measuring 72 cm long is cut equally into three pieces. The shorter pieces of wire are bent to make three identical triangles of equal sides. What is the length of one side of a triangle?

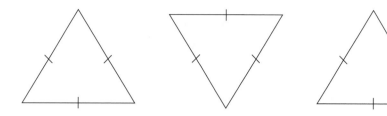

8. Given that ☐ + △ = 110

and ☐ + △ + △ = 200,

find the value of ☐ and of △.

9. What is the area of the figure drawn on the square grid?

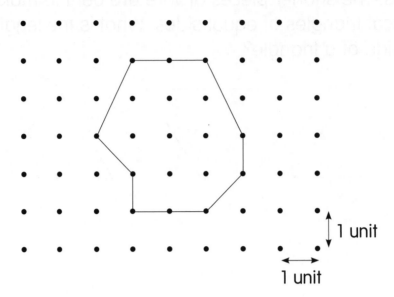

1 unit

1 unit

10. Susan spent $\frac{1}{3}$ of her pocket money on food and $\frac{1}{2}$ of what was left on a drink. If she had $10 left, how much was her pocket money?

Worked Example 1

Tommy was lining up to buy concert tickets. He was 29th in the line. From the back of the line, he was in the 34th position. How many people were there in the line?

Since Tommy was 29th from the front, there were 28 people in front of him. Since he was 34th from the back, there were 33 people behind him.

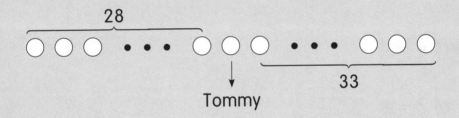

$$28 + 1 + 33 = 62$$

There were **62** people in the line.

Worked Example 2

The figure below is made up of 6 squares. Divide the figure into 4 identical shapes.

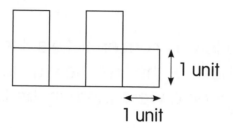

1 unit

1 unit

The figure is made up of 6 squares.
The area of the figure is 6 square units.

$\frac{1}{4}$ of 4 = 1

$\frac{1}{4}$ of 2 = $\frac{1}{2}$

The area of each shape will be $1\frac{1}{2}$ square units.

One possible division is as follows:

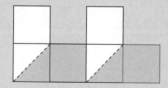

Answer all questions. Show your work and write your statements clearly.

1. Some llamas are walking over the hill. One llama is in front of three llamas. One llama is behind three llamas. Two llamas are between the other llamas. What is the fewest number of llamas that are walking over the hill?

   Hint: Draw a diagram, then guess and check until the conditions are satisfied.

2. How many times does the digit "1" appear in numbers from 1 to 100?

3. Veronica spent $9.90 on a book. She spent $6.35 more on a teddy bear than the book. If she had $2.20 left, how much money did she have at first?

4. Joel was in a line at an amusement park to take a ride. He was the 36th person from the front and 43rd person from the back of the line. How many people were in the line?

   Hint: See worked Example 1.

5. John had a bagel, as shown below. He shared his bagel with four friends. He used only 2 straight cuts to divide the bagel into five pieces. If each piece was not of the same size, how did he divide the bagel into 5 pieces?

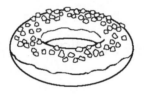

6. Alfred is 6 years older than his sister. Five years ago, he was 11 years old. How old is his sister now?

7. Irene bought 15 packs of snacks, each weighing 3 oz.
   Theresa bought 9 packs of snacks, each weighing 5 oz.
   (a) How many ounces of snacks did they buy in total?
   (b) One of the girls dropped some packs of snacks while
       they were walking home. They found that they had
       20 oz less snacks.
       (i) Who dropped her snacks?
       (ii) How many packs were dropped?

   Hint: Can 3-kg or 5-kg packs sum up to 20 kg?

8. Rose made a necklace with different colored beads.
   She followed a pattern: 2 red beads, 1 blue bead, then
   1 green bead. The pattern is repeated and she used a
   total of 5 green beads to make the necklace. How many
   beads did she use altogether?

9. One kilogram of grade A flour costs $6.50. One kilogram of grade B flour costs $4.00. Two kilograms of grade A flour are mixed with three kilograms of grade B flour to produce grade C flour. How much does one kilogram of grade C flour cost?

10. There were 13 cars and bicycles in a parking lot. If there were 44 wheels altogether, how many cars were in the parking lot?

11. The figure below is made up of 4 identical squares. Divide the figure into 4 equal parts using only two cuts.

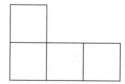

14 Review Questions 2

Worked Example 1

 In the figure below, the perimeter of the rectangle is twice that of the square. What is the perimeter of the rectangle?

6 cm

Perimeter of square = 4 × 6 cm
= 24 cm

Perimeter of rectangle = 2 × 24 cm
= 48 cm

The perimeter of the rectangle is **48 cm**.

Worked Example 2

How many digits are used to print the page numbers in *Math Can Be Fun*, which has 200 pages?

Page numbers	Number of digits
1 – 9	**9**
10 – 99	99 – 10 + 1 = 90 90 × 2 = **180**
100 – 200	200 – 100 + 1 = 101 101 × 3 = **303**

9 + 180 + 303 = 492

492 digits are used to print the page numbers in *Math Can Be Fun*.

Note: We need to "add one" when it comes to finding the number of page numbers.

Practice Questions

Answer all questions. Show your work and write your statements clearly.

1. Write down the next two terms in each sequence.

   (a) 1, 1, 2, 3, 5, 8, 13, _____, _____

   (b) 1, 4, 9, 16, _____, _____

2. What fraction of each figure is shaded?
   (a)   (b)   (c)

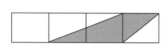
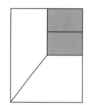

3. Joseph left school and took 1 h 35 min to reach home. If he reached home at 5:30 P.M., at what time did he leave school?

4. Eddy's score on a math test is in the 14th position from both the highest and the lowest scores. How many students took the test?

5. The total mass of a mango and a guava is 1,350 g. The guava is 580 g heavier than the mango. What is the mass of the mango?

   Hint: Draw a model.

6. Ian had three large identical boxes to contain three different types of balls as shown below. If each box is completely filled with only one type of ball, find the box with the
   (a) least number of balls,
   (b) the most number of balls.

7. Five friends met at a concert. Each person shook hands with the other four. How many handshakes took place?

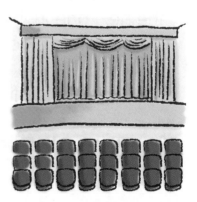

8. A farmer picked 1,200 apples from his orchard. He gave away 240 apples to his relatives and packed the rest into bags of 8 each.
   (a) How many bags of apples were there altogether?
   (b) If he sold each bag of apples for $3, how much money did he collect?

9. The area of two parts of a circle is given below. What is the area of the shaded part?

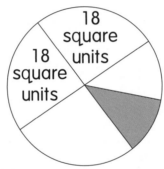

Hint: What fraction of the circle represents the shaded part?

10. Five children are in a line to see the dentist. Dennis is the next one in line. Cathy is standing behind Aaron. Aaron is two places in front of Betty. Esther is in line next to Aaron. List the order of the five children in the line starting with the first one.

Hint: Draw a number line to order the position of each child.

Challenging Problems

Worked Example

Jenny walked from her house to school and then to the library. After borrowing some books from the library, she walked home using the same route. What was the total distance she traveled? Express your answer in kilometers and meters.

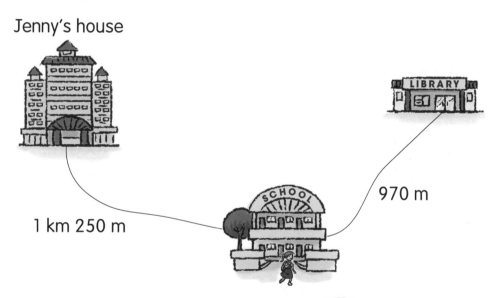

Jenny's house

1 km 250 m

970 m

$$
\begin{array}{c}
\text{1 km 250 m} \qquad\qquad \text{970 m} \\
\text{House} \longleftrightarrow \text{School} \longleftrightarrow \text{Library} \\
\text{1 km 250 m} \qquad\qquad \text{970 m}
\end{array}
$$

1 km 250 m + 1 km 250 m + 970 m + 970 m
= 4 km 440 m

Jenny traveled a total distance of **4 km 440 m**.

Answer all questions. Show your work and write your statements clearly.

1. At a stadium, there were 4,054 children and 128 teachers. The number of parents was 3,656 fewer than the total number of children and teachers. How many parents were there?

2. A six-sided die rests on a table. When Rose walks around the table, she counts and adds the dots on all the faces of the die that she can see. There is a total of 16 dots. What is the number of dots on the face resting on the table?

3. The letters A, B, and C below stand for different digits. Which digit does each letter represent?

$$\begin{array}{r} B\ A \\ +\ B\ A \\ \hline C\ A\ A \end{array}$$

Hint: C must be 1.

4. How many three-digit numbers are there, such that the ones digit and hundreds digit are the same, but the tens digit is three more than the ones digit?

5. Signal lights are located 25 m apart along a tunnel. There is a total of 8 signal lights in the tunnel. If there are signal lights at the beginning and end of the tunnel, how long is the tunnel?

   Hint: How many intervals are there?

6. Use the digits 0, 2, 4, 5, 6, and 7 to fill the following boxes to obtain the greatest possible difference.

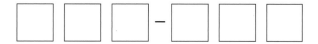

7. Cynthia had $16.75. She withdrew more cash from an ATM before shopping. After spending $17.50 on a box of cookies and $23.40 on a box of chocolates, she had $35.85 left. How much money did she withdraw from the ATM?

8. Mr. Smith bought a new television set for $304 and saved $9 on his electricity bill each month, as compared to using an old television set. How many months of savings on his electricity bill will allow him to get a second television of the same price?

9. What is the largest two-digit number that can be divided by 2 and 3 without any remainder?

10. A rectangle with an area of 36 square units is shown below.

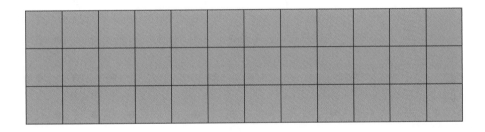

How many ways can you arrange 36 such square units to form a rectangle? (Assume that a square is not treated as a rectangle.)

11. The figure below is made up of squares. If the perimeter of each square is 12 cm, find the perimeter of the figure.

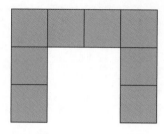

12. Study the sequence below.

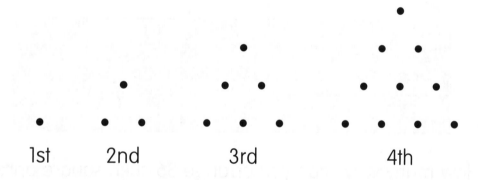

   1st   2nd   3rd   4th

(a) Draw the 5th figure.
(b) How many dots are there in the 10th figure?

15 Review Questions 3

Worked Example 1

A total of 852 digits are used to print the page numbers of a book. How many pages does the book have?

Page numbers	Number of digits
1 – 9	9
10 – 99	99 – 10 + 1 = 90 90 × 2 = 180

852 – 9 – 180 = 663

663 digits are used for 3-digit page numbers.

663 ÷ 3 = 221

There are 221 3-digit pages.

221 + 9 + 90 = 320

The book has **320** pages.

Worked Example 2

How many digits are there in all the numbers from 1 to 500?

Numbers	Number of digits
1 – 9	9
10 – 99	99 – 10 + 1 = 90 90 × 2 = 180
100 – 500	500 – 100 + 1 = 401 401 × 3 = 1,203

9 + 180 + 1,203 = 1,392

There are **1,392** digits.

Practice Questions

Answer all questions. Show your work and write your statements clearly.

1. There were 18 people in a line at a ticket counter. 10 people were in line behind John. How many people were in line in front of him?

2. A snail falls into a well that is 11 meters deep. During the day, it can crawl up 3 meters. At night, it slips down by 1 meter. How many days will it take the snail to get out of the well?

   Hint: Draw a number line.

3. Tracy plans to buy a plasma TV that costs $1,395. When she counts her savings, she realizes that she is short $165. How much money does she have?

4. A movie lasts 1 hour 18 minutes. At what time must the movie start so that it will end by midnight?

5. Elizabeth has 300 more buttons than Paul at first. She gives 150 buttons to him. Who has more buttons now?

6. I am thinking of a number that is less than 1,000 but greater than 459. The hundreds digit is even and is 2 less than the ones digit. The tens digit is half the ones digit. What number am I thinking of?

7. The diagram below shows the scores on a dart board.

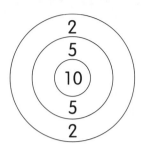

Arthur scored 21 points. What is the least number of darts needed to achieve that score?

8. Look at the figures below. Then fill in the missing numbers in the boxes.

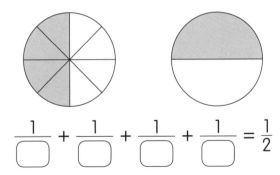

$$\frac{1}{\square} + \frac{1}{\square} + \frac{1}{\square} + \frac{1}{\square} = \frac{1}{2}$$

Worked Example

A survey was conducted among a group of students on their favorite type of movie. Students were given a choice of 5 types.

Study the bar graph and answer the following questions.

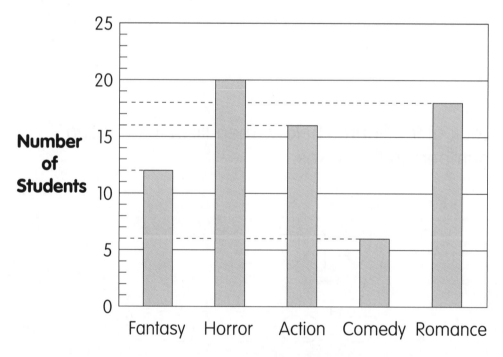

Type of Movie

(a) How many more students preferred horror movies to comedy movies?

(b) How many students preferred fantasy or romance movies in all?

(c) The number of students who liked romance movies is three times the number of students who liked comedy movies.

Is the statement true or false? Explain your answer.

(d) How many students took part in the survey?

(e) The total number of students who liked horror and action movies was more than the total number of students who liked fantasy, romance and comedy movies.

Is the statement true or false? Explain your answer.

(a) The bar graph shows that 20 students liked horror movies and 6 students liked comedy movies.

20 − 6 = 14

14 more students preferred horror movies to comedy movies.

(b) The bar graph shows that 12 students liked fantasy movies and 18 students liked romance movies altogether.

12 + 18 = 30

30 students preferred fantasy or romance movies in all.

(c) The statement is **true**.

The bar graph shows that, 18 students liked romance movies and 6 liked comedy movies.

$18 \div 6 = 3$

Therefore, the number of students who liked romance movies is three times the number of students who liked comedy movies.

(d)

Type of movies	Number of students
Fantasy	12
Horror	20
Action	16
Comedy	6
Romance	18
Total	72

$12 + 20 + 16 + 6 + 18 = 72$

72 students took part in the survey.

(e) The total number of students who liked horror and action movies is $20 + 16 = 36$.

The total number of students who liked fantasy, romance, and comedy movies is $12 + 18 + 6 = 36$.

The statement is **false**.

The total number of students who liked horror and action movies was the same as the total number of students who liked fantasy, romance, and comedy movies.

Answer all questions. Show your work and write your statements clearly.

1. Jenny has $100 in her money box now. If she saves $10 every month, how much will she have in her money box after one year?

2. Arthur bought some pears. He gave the fruit seller a $50 bill and received $38 change. If 3 pears cost $1, how many pears did he buy altogether?

3. Fill in the circles with numbers from 1 to 9 such that the sum of the numbers along each line is 15. Use each number only once.

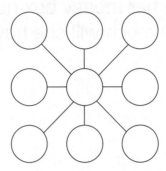

Hint: Look for sets of three numbers that add up to 15.

4. Hamid delivered some snakes and spiders to a zoo. The zookeeper counted 48 legs and 22 heads. How many snakes and how many spiders were there?

5. A straight cut will slice a circle into 2 pieces; two cuts will slice a circle into a maximum of 4 pieces. What is the most number of pieces that can be obtained from 5 straight cuts? The pieces need not be of the same sizes.

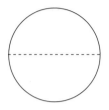

1 cut, 2 pieces

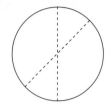

2 cuts, 4 pieces

6. Study the diagrams below. Then fill in the boxes with the correct numbers.

(a)

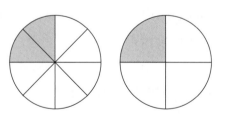

$$\frac{1}{8} = \frac{1}{4} - \frac{1}{\boxed{}}$$

(b)

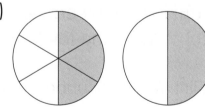

$$\frac{1}{6} + \frac{1}{6} = \frac{1}{2} - \frac{1}{\boxed{}}$$

7. Four students, Ann, Jean, Karen and Sue, borrowed books from a library. Each person was allowed to borrow a maximum of six books. They borrowed a total of 15 books. Karen borrowed two books and Jean borrowed three books. How many books did Ann borrow if Sue borrowed the most number of books?

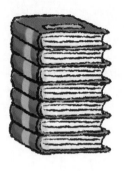

8. Lisa bought 11 pens and erasers for $5.00. A pen cost 50¢ and an eraser cost 40¢.
   (a) How many erasers did she buy?
   (b) What is the total cost of the pens?

   Hint: Make a supposition, or use guess and check.

9. The figure below shows a square formed by 4 identical rectangles. The perimeter of each rectangle is 50 cm. What is the length of the square?

10. During a marathon, 46 cups of water were consumed by 13 children. If each girl drank 3 cups of water and each boy drank 4 cups of water, how many boys and how many girls were there?

Hint: Make a supposition, or use guess and check.

11. Albert cut a wire into two pieces to make the following rectangles.

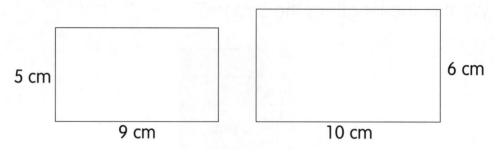

5 cm

9 cm

6 cm

10 cm

What is the length of the original wire?

12. How many right angles are there in the figure below?

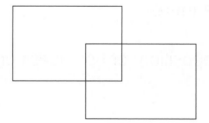

Answers

1 Addition and Subtraction

Practice Questions (pp. 4-5)

1.

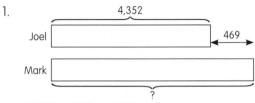

4,352 + 469 = 4,821
Mark collected **4,821** stamps.
Caution: Words like "less" and "fewer" do not always mean "to subtract" or "minus."

2. (a) 2,450 – 896 = 2,450 – 900 + 4
   $\qquad\qquad$ = 2,450 – 1,000 + 100 + 4
   $\qquad\qquad$ = 1,450 + 100 + 4
   $\qquad\qquad$ = 1,550 + 4
   $\qquad\qquad$ = 1,554
   There are **1,554** men.
   (b) 1,554 – 896 = 1,554 – 900 + 4
   $\qquad\qquad$ = 654 + 4
   $\qquad\qquad$ = 658
   There are **658** more men than women.

3. *Method 1*
   $997 + $498 = $1,000 + $498 – $3
   $\qquad\qquad$ = $1,498 – $3
   $\qquad\qquad$ = $1,495
   The plasma TV cost **$1,495**.

   Method 2
   $997 + $498 = $1,000 + $500 – $3 – $2
   $\qquad\qquad$ = $1,500 – $5
   $\qquad\qquad$ = $1,495
   The plasma TV cost **$1,495**.

4. (10, 20, 30, 40, 50, 60, 70, 80, 90, 100)
   The digit "0" appears **11 times**.

5. 1st showtime: 947 people watched.
   1,210 – 139 = 1,071
   2nd showtime: 1,071 people watched.
   947 + 1,071 = 2,018
   2,018 people watched the two movie showtimes altogether.

6. *Before*

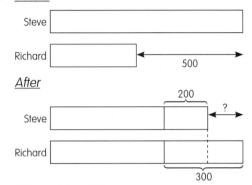

   After

   500 – 300 = 200
   300 – 200 = 100
   Richard has **100** more marbles than Steve now.

Challenging Problems (pp. 8-11)

1.

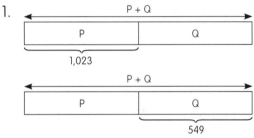

   (a) P = **1,023**
   (b) Q = **549**
   (c) P + Q = 1,023 + 549
   $\qquad\quad$ = **1,572**

2. The age difference between them at any time is always 18.

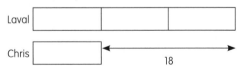

   2 units = 18
   1 unit = 9
   Chris will be **9** years old.
   Check: Chris = 9 $\quad$ Laval = 9 x 3 = 27
   $\qquad\qquad\qquad\qquad$ 27 – 9 = 18

3. *Method 1*

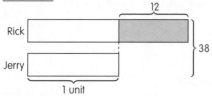

2 units + 12 = 38
2 units = 38 − 12 = 26
1 unit = 26 ÷ 2 = 13
Jerry has **13** toy cars.

Method 2

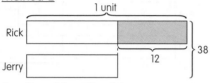

2 units = 38 + 12 = 50
1 unit = 50 ÷ 2 = 25
25 − 12 = 13
Jerry has **13** toy cars.

4. 9, 19, 29, …, 89, 90, 91, …, 99
    The digit "9" appears **20 times**.

5. Q + S = 9
    P + R = 15
    P + Q + R + S = 9 + 15 = **24**

6. *Method 1* (Guess and check)
    A cat has 4 legs.
    A flamingo has 2 legs.

Number of wild cats	Number of flamingoes	Total number of legs
9	6	9 × 4 + 6 × 2 = 36 + 12 = 48 (too high)
8	7	8 × 4 + 7 × 2 = 32 + 14 = 46 (still high)
7	8	7 × 4 + 8 × 2 = 28 + 16 = 44 ✔

There are **7** wild cats.

Note: The table shows 3 guesses and checks. However, we may get the answer in fewer or more than 3 tries.
First, make an intelligent guess, then try to increase or decrease one of the numbers, until you arrive at the correct sum, which is 44.

Method 2
Suppose there was a total of 15 flamingoes. Then the total number of legs would be 15 × 2 = 30.
There are a total of 44 legs, so the extra 44 − 30 = 14 legs must have come from the wild cats.
One wild cat has 2 more legs than one flamingo.
Thus, there must be 14 ÷ 2 = 7 wild cats, and 15 − 7 = 8 flamingoes.
There are **7** wild cats.
Check: 7 × 4 + 8 × 2 = 28 + 16 = 44

7.

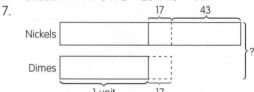

1 unit = 17 + 43 = 60
3 units = 3 × 60 = 180
Number of coins left = 180 coins
He had **180** coins left.

8.

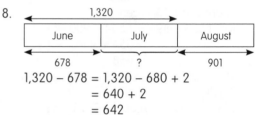

1,320 − 678 = 1,320 − 680 + 2
= 640 + 2
= 642
He sold 642 loaves of bread in July.
901 − 642 = 901 − 641 − 1
= 260 − 1
= 259
He sold **259** more loaves in August than in July.

9. Digit "6" in the ones place: 6, 16, 26, …, 96-10 times
    Digit "6" in the tens place: 60, 61, …, 69-10 times
    10 + 10 = 20
    20 whole numbers between 1 and 100 contain the digit "6".

10.

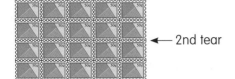 ← 1st tear

 ← 2nd tear

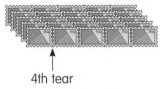 ← 3rd tear

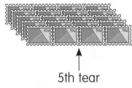

↑
4th tear

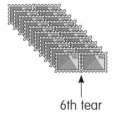

↑
5th tear

↑
6th tear

The least number of times is **6**.

2 Multiplication and Division

Practice Questions (pp. 15-17)

1. $8 \times 6 + 5 \times 7 = 48 + 35$
   $= 83$
   8 students and 5 teachers receive **83** coins.

2. $120 \div 8 = (120 \div 4) \div (8 \div 4)$
   $= 30 \div 2$
   $= 15$ pens
   Each child received **15** pens.

3. $544 \div 8 = 68$
   Each box has 68 apples.
   $68 - 29 = 69 - 29 - 1$
   $\qquad\quad = 40 - 1$
   $\qquad\quad = 39$
   39 apples would be left in the box.

4. Total number of coins $= 7 \times 126 = 882$
   Number of coins in each bigger
   bag $= 882 \div 3 = 294$
   Each bigger bag will contain **294** coins.

5. $36 \times 4 = 72 \times 2 = 144$
   Bobby gives 144 postcards away.
   $345 - 144 = 344 - 144 + 1$
   $\qquad\qquad = 200 + 1$
   $\qquad\qquad = 201$
   He has **201** postcards left.

6.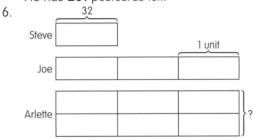

   1 unit = 32
   6 units = $6 \times 32 = 192$
   Arlette has **192** stickers.

7. $42 + 50 = 92$
   $120 - 92 = 120 - 90 - 2$
   $\qquad\qquad = 30 - 2$
   $\qquad\qquad = 28$
   Each album has 28 Mexico stamps.
   $6 \times 28 = 168$
   6 such albums have **168** Mexico stamps in total.

8. Ann and Sally make a total of $1 + 2 = 3$ paper cranes each time.
   $141 = 120 + 21$
   $\quad\; = 3 \times 40 + 3 \times 7$
   $141 \div 3 = 40 + 7 = 47$
   Ann made 47 cranes.
   $47 + 47 = 94$
   Sally made **94** cranes.

Challenging Problems (pp. 20-24)

1.
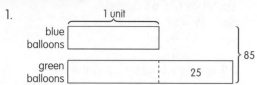

2 units = 85 − 25 = 60
1 unit = 60 ÷ 2 = 30
1 unit + 25 = 30 + 25 = 55
She will take home **30** blue balloons and **55** green balloons.

2. *Method 1*

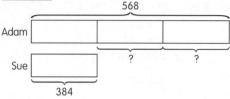

568 − 384 = 184
184 ÷ 2 = 92
384 + 92 = 476
Each of them has **476** postcards now.

Method 2
568 + 384 = 952
Adam and Sue have 852 postcards altogether.
952 ÷ 2 = 476
Each of them has **476** postcards now.

3.

There are 8 cars, but 7 intervals.
Total length of 8 cars = 8 × 16 m = 128 m
Total distance between the cars
= 142 m − 128 m = 14 m
Distance between two neighboring cars
= 14 m ÷ 7 = 2 m
The distance between two neighboring cars is **2 m**.

4. 48 × 2 = 96
120 − 96 = 24
3 coaches are needed:
2 coaches, each filled with 48 passengers, and 1 coach filled with 24 remaining passengers.
48 − 24 = 24
24 seats will be unoccupied.

5. Number of candies Mrs. Jiminez gave away = 84 − 8 = 76
76 ÷ 4 = 38 ÷ 2 = 19
19 students received candies from Mrs. Jiminez.

6. *Method 1*

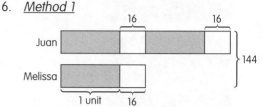

3 units = 144 − 16 − 16 − 16
= 96
1 unit = 96 ÷ 3 = 32
Number of coins Juan had at first
= 32 + 16 + 32 + 16 + 16
= 112
Juan had **112** coins at first.

Method 2
After

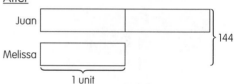

Before

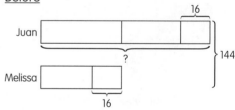

3 units = 144
1 unit = 144 ÷ 3 = 48
2 units + 16 = 2 × 48 + 16
= 96 + 16
= 112
Juan had **112** coins at first.

7. *Method 1*

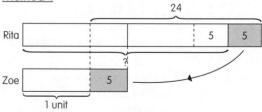

1 unit = 24 − 5 − 5 − 5 = 9
1 unit + 5 = 9 + 5 = 14
2 × 14 = 28
Rita had **28** barrettes left.

Method 2

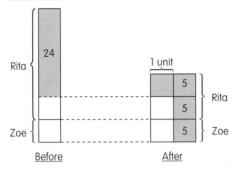

Before   After

1 unit + 5 + 5 + 5 = 24
1 unit = 24 − 15 = 9
2 units + 5 + 5 = 2 × 9 + 10
$$= 18 + 10$$
$$= 28$$
Rita had **28** barrettes left.

8. 2 + 3 = 5 ⟶ 1 group of 5 cans
   30 ÷ 5 = 6
   There are 6 groups of 5 cans.
   6 × 2 = 12 and 6 × 3 = 18
   Jason picked up **12** cans and Louis picked up **18** cans.

9.
No. of red envelopes	No. of stamps	No. of blue envelopes	No. of stickers
1	6	1	5
2	12	2	10
3	18	3	15
4	24	4	20
5	**30**	5	25
		6	**30**

5 red envelopes have 30 stamps, and **6** blue envelopes have 30 stickers.

10.
Small rocks	Large rocks	Number of rock bears
5	1	1
10	2	2
15	3	3
20	4	4

All 20 small rocks, but only 4 out of the 9 large rocks, will be used to make 4 rock bears.
Jack can make **4** rock bears.

3   Mental Calculation

Practice Questions (p. 28)

1. 56 + 9 = 56 + 10 − 1
   $$= 66 − 1$$
   $$= \textbf{65}$$
2. 728 + 98 = 726 + 2 + 98
   $$= 726 + 100$$
   $$= \textbf{826}$$
3. 145 − 99 = 146 − 1 − 99
   $$= 146 − 100$$
   $$= \textbf{46}$$
4. 706 − 198 = 706 − 200 + 2
   $$= 506 + 2$$
   $$= \textbf{508}$$
5. 505 × 9 = 500 × 9 + 5 × 9
   $$= 4,500 + 45$$
   $$= \textbf{4,545}$$
6. 82 × 6 = 80 × 6 + 2 × 6
   $$= 480 + 12$$
   $$= \textbf{492}$$
7. 198 + 243 = 198 + 2 + 241
   $$= 200 + 241$$
   $$= \textbf{441}$$
8. *Method 1*
   752 − 303 = 752 − 300 − 3
   $$= 452 − 3$$
   $$= 452 − 2 − 1$$
   $$= 450 − 1$$
   $$= \textbf{449}$$

   Method 2
   752 − 303 = (752 − 3) − (303 − 3)
   $$= 749 − 300$$
   $$= \textbf{449}$$
9. 57 × 3 = 50 × 3 + 7 × 3
   $$= 150 + 21$$
   $$= \textbf{171}$$

Challenging Problems (pp. 32-33)

1. 158 + 93 + 42 = 158 + 42 + 93
   $$= 200 + 93$$
   $$= \textbf{293}$$
2. 997 + 605 = 997 + 3 + 602
   $$= 1,000 + 602$$
   $$= \textbf{1,602}$$
3. 74 + 37 + 49
   $$= 70 + 1 + 3 + 37 + 49$$
   $$= 70 + 40 + 50$$
   $$= \textbf{160}$$

4. 234 + 567
   = 200 + 34 + 500 + 66 + 1
   = 700 + 100 + 1
   = **801**
5. 7,000 − 137
   = 6,999 − 137 + 1
   = 6,862 + 1
   = **6,863**
6. 10,000 − 894
   = 9,999 − 894 + 1
   = 9,105 + 1
   = **9,106**
7. 126 − 75
   = 100 + 26 − 75
   = 26 + 25
   = **51**
8. 163 − 92
   = 100 + 63 − 92
   = 63 + 8
   = **71**
9. 58 × 2 = 50 × 2 + 8 × 2
   = 100 + 16
   = **116**
10. 750 × 2 = 700 × 2 + 50 × 2
    = 1,400 + 100
    = **1,500**
11. 92 ÷ 2 = 90 ÷ 2 + 2 ÷ 2
    = 45 + 1
    = **46**
12. 740 ÷ 2 = 700 ÷ 2 + 40 ÷ 2
    = 350 + 20
    = **370**
13. 85 × 5 = 85 × 10 ÷ 2
    = 850 ÷ 2
    = **425**
14. 462 × 5 = 462 × 10 ÷ 2
    = 4,620 ÷ 2
    = **2,310**
15. 620 ÷ 5 = 600 ÷ 5 + 20 ÷ 5
    = 120 + 4
    = **124**
16. 905 ÷ 5 = 900 ÷ 5 + 5 ÷ 5
    = 180 + 1
    = **181**

4 Length

Practice Questions (pp. 37-39)

1.
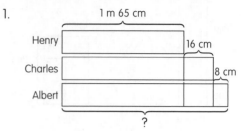

   1 m 65 cm + 16 cm + 8 cm
   = 1 m 65 cm + 24 cm
   = 1 m 89 cm
   Albert is **1 m 89 cm** tall.

2.
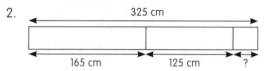

   Method 1
   325 cm − 165 cm − 125 cm
   = 325 cm − 125 cm − 165 cm
   = 200 cm − 165 cm
   = 35 cm
   Robin had **35 cm** of string left.

   Method 2
   165 cm + 125 cm = 290 cm
   325 cm − 290 cm
   = 325 cm − 300 cm + 10 cm
   = 25 cm + 10 cm
   = 35 cm
   Robin had **35 cm** of string left.

3.
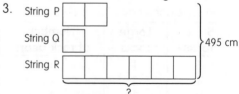

   9 units = 495 cm
   1 unit = 495 cm ÷ 9 = 55 cm
   6 units = 6 × 55 cm = 330 cm
   Length of string R = 330 cm or 3 m 30 cm
   The length of string R is **330 cm**.

4.

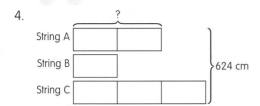

6 units = 624 cm
1 unit = 624 cm ÷ 6
      = 104 cm
2 units = 2 × 104 cm = 208 cm = 2 m 8 cm
The length of string A is **2 m 8 cm**.

5.

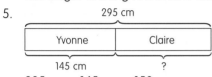

295 cm − 145 cm = 150 cm
Claire is 150 cm tall.

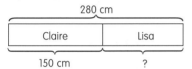

280 cm − 150 cm = 130 cm
130 cm = 100 cm + 30 cm
       = 1 m + 30 cm
Lisa is **1 m 30 cm**.

6. 10 ft 2 in. − 5 ft 4 in. = 4 ft 10 in.
Kelly is 4 ft 10 in. tall.
5 ft. 4 in. − 4 ft 10 in. = 6 in.
Adeline is taller than Kelly by **6 in**.

7.

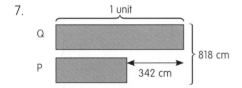

2 units = 818 cm + 342 cm = 1,160 cm
1 unit = 1,160 cm ÷ 2 = 580 cm
580 cm = 500 m 80 cm
       = 5 m 80 cm
Length of string Q = 5 m 80 cm
The length of string Q is **5 m 80 cm**.

8.

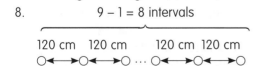

8 × 120 cm = 960 cm
960 cm = 9 m 60 cm
The distance between the first and last
tree is **9 m 60 cm**.

Challenging Problems (pp. 42-44)

1.

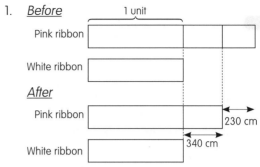

1 unit = 340 cm + 230 cm = 570 cm
2 units = 2 × 570 cm = 1,140 cm
The pink ribbon was **11 m 40 cm** long at
first.

2.

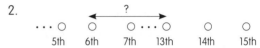

From the 6th to the third last (13th) lamp
posts, there are 13 − 6 = 7 intervals.
Each interval is 500 m.
7 intervals is 7 × 500 m = 3,500 m
= 3 km 500 m
The distance between the 6th and the
3rd last lamp posts is **3 km 500 m**.

3.

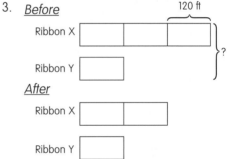

1 unit = 120 ft
4 units = 4 × 120 ft = 480 ft
Total length of ribbons X and Y at first
= 480 ft = 480 ÷ 3 yd = 160 yd
The total length of ribbons X and Y was
160 yd at first.

4.

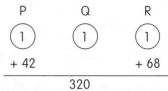

Bob & Mark: 5 ft 6 in. | 4 ft 7 in.

June & Anne: 4 ft 9 in. | ? with 3 in.

5 ft 6 in. + 4 ft 7 in. − 3 in. = 9 ft 10 in.
The total height of June and Anne is 9 ft 10 in.
9 ft 10 in. − 4 ft 9 in. = 5 ft 1 in.
The height of Anne is **5 ft 1 in.**

5.

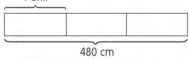

String A — 1 unit, 1 yd
String B — 13 ft 4 in.
String C — 1 ft 8 in.

3 ft − 1 ft 8 in. = 1 ft 4 in.

3 units = 13 ft 4 in. − 3 ft − 1 ft 4 in. = 9 ft
1 unit = 9 ft ÷ 3 = 3 ft
Length of string A = 3 ft or 1 yd.
The length of string A is **3 ft**.

6.

1 unit

480 cm

3 units = 480 cm
1 unit = 480 cm ÷ 3 = 160 cm
160 cm = 100 cm + 60 cm
= 1 m 60 cm
The length of each side of the triangle is **1 m 60 cm**.

7. *Method 1*

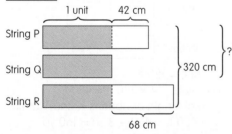

1 unit | 42 cm
String P
String Q — 320 cm — ?
String R
68 cm

3 units = 320 cm − 42 cm − 68 cm
= 210 cm
1 unit = 210 cm ÷ 3 = 70 cm
Length of string Q = 70 cm
Length of string P = 70 cm + 42 cm
= 112 cm
Total length of strings P and Q
= 112 cm + 70 cm
= 182 cm
= 1 m 82 cm

The total length of strings P and Q is **1 m 82 cm**.

Method 2
1. *Grasp the concept*

Let ① represent the length of Q.

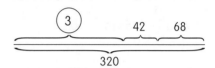

P: ① | Q: ① | R: ①
+ 42 | | + 68
320

2. *Diagram*

③ | 42 | 68
320

3. *Number sentences*

① + ① + ① = ③

42 + 68 = 110
320 − 110 = 210
210 ÷ 3 = 70 → ①
① + 42 = 70 + 42 = 112
112 + 70 = 182
The total length of P and Q is **1 m 82 cm**.

8.

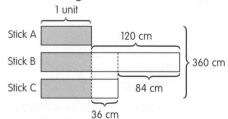

1 unit
Stick A — 120 cm
Stick B — 360 cm
Stick C — 84 cm
36 cm

120 − 84 = 36
3 units = 360 cm − 120 cm − 36 cm
= 204 cm
1 unit = 204 cm ÷ 3 = 68 cm
Length of stick A = 68 cm
Length of stick C = 68 cm + 36 cm
= 104 cm
Total length of sticks A and C
= 68 cm + 104 cm
= 172 cm
= 1 m 72 cm
The total length of sticks A and C is **1 m 72 cm**.

5 Mass and Weight

Practice Questions (pp. 48–50)

1.
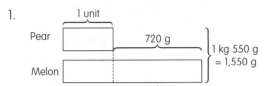

2 units = 1,550 g – 720 g = 830 g
1 unit = 830 g ÷ 2 = 415 g
The mass of the pear is **415 g**.

2. 1 apple weighs 5 oz.
9 apples weigh 9 × 5 oz = 45 oz.
3 lb = 3 × 16 oz = 48 oz
48 oz – 45 oz = 3 oz
The weight of the box is **3 oz**.

3.
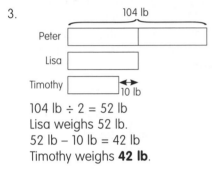

104 lb ÷ 2 = 52 lb
Lisa weighs 52 lb.
52 lb – 10 lb = 42 lb
Timothy weighs **42 lb**.

4.

Tom / George — 1 unit, 248 lb, 36 lb

2 units = 248 lb + 36 lb
1 unit = 124 lb + 18 lb = 142 lb
Tom's weight is **142 lb**.

5.
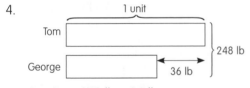

3 units = 555 g
1 unit = 555 g ÷ 3 = 185 g
4 units = 4 × 185 g = 400 + 320 + 20
= 740 g
The total weight of the guava and the
apple is **740 g**.

6. *Method 1*
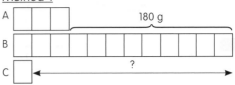

9 units = 180 g
1 unit = 180 g ÷ 9 = 20 g
10 units = 10 × 20 g = 200 g
11 units = 20 g + 200 g = 220 g
Bag C is **220 g** lighter than bag B.

Method 2
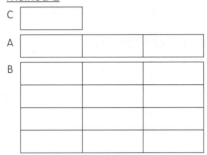

12 units – 3 units = 180 g
9 units = 180 g
1 unit = 180 g ÷ 9 = 20 g
11 units = 11 × 20 g = 220 g
Bag C is **220 g** lighter than bag B.

7. 10 full crates of peanuts weigh 220 kg.
1 full crate of peanuts weighs 220 kg ÷ 10
= 22 kg
Empty crate + peanuts = 22 kg
22 kg – 5 kg = 17 kg
The mass of the peanuts in each crate is
17 kg.

8. 456 g + 210 g + 306 g = 972 g
June, Ann, and Joyce have a total of 972 g
of flour.
972 g ÷ 3 = 324 g
Each person will have 324 g of flour.
456 g – 324 g = 132 g
June must give **132 g** of flour to Ann and
Joyce.

9.

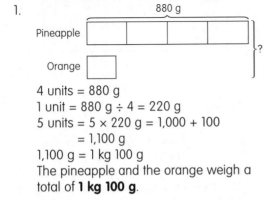

4 lb 6 oz – 2 lb 10 oz = 1 lb 12 oz
Keith's bag is 1 lb 12 oz heavier than
Sue's bag.
20 lb 5 oz + 1 lb 12 oz = 22 lb 1 oz
Keith's bag weighs **22 lb 1 oz**.

Challenging Problems (pp. 54–57)

1.

Pineapple | 880 g
Orange

?

4 units = 880 g
1 unit = 880 g ÷ 4 = 220 g
5 units = 5 × 220 g = 1,000 + 100
          = 1,100 g
1,100 g = 1 kg 100 g
The pineapple and the orange weigh a
total of **1 kg 100 g**.

Note: "3" times more than" means "four times
as much."

2. Instead of adding all the masses on both
sides of the scale, eliminate common
masses on both sides. Then work out
with the remaining masses by equating
each side.
50 g + 50 g + X = 200 g
      100 g + X = 200 g
              X = 100 g
The mass of X is **100 g**.

3. (a) The lightest item is the carrots (275 g).
The heaviest item is the beef
(1,350 g).
1,350 g + 275 g = 1,625 g
The total mass of the lightest and the
heaviest items is **1 kg 625 g**.

(b) 725 g + 310 g + 275 g + 1,350 g + 530 g +290 g
= 725 g + 275 g + 310 g + 290 g + 1,350 g + 530 g
= 1,000 g + 600 g + 1,880 g
= 1,600 g + 1,880 g
= 3,480 g
  3,480 g = 3,000 g + 480 g
          = 3 kg 480 g
The total mass of all the items is **3 kg
480 g**.

(c) 725 g + 1,350 g = 2,075 g
3,480 g – 2,075 g = 1,405 g
1,405 g = 1 kg 405 g
The total mass of the remaining items
Mrs. Yong needs to carry is **1 kg
405 g**.

4.

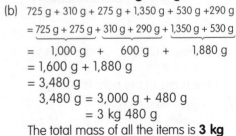

64 lb – 18 lb = 64 lb – 20 lb + 2 lb
              = 44 lb + 2 lb
              = 46 lb
Bag B weighs 46 lb.
64 lb + 46 lb = 110 lb
Bags A and B weigh a total of 110 lb.
2 × 110 lb = 220 lb
Bag C weighs **220 lb**.

5. 2 times more = 3 times as much as

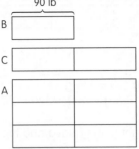

1 unit = 90 lb
6 units = 6 × 90 lb = 540 lb
Box A weighs **540 lb**.

6.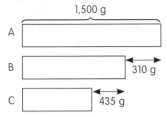

(a) 1,500 g – 310 g = 1,500 g – 300 g – 10 g
                      = 1,200 g – 10 g
                      = 1,190 g
   The mass of item B is **1,190 g**.
(b) 1,190 – 435 = 755
   The mass of item C is **755 g**.
(c) 1,500 – 755 = 745
   The difference in mass between
   items A and C is **745 g**.

7.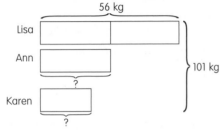

(a) 56 kg ÷ 2 = 28 kg
   Ann's mass is **28 kg**.
(b) 101 kg – 56 kg – 28 kg = 101 kg – 84 kg
                          = 17 kg
   Karen's mass is **17 kg**.

8. 1 ▢ = 3 ◯ (given)

   2 ▢ = 2 × 3 ◯ = 6 ◯

   3 △ = 2 ▢ (given)

   3 △ = 6 ◯

   1 △ = 2 ◯

   1 triangle and **2 circles** will balance both
   sides of the scales.

6   Capacity

Practice Questions (pp. 61–63)

1.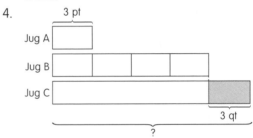

   2 × 2 L 250 mL = 4 L 500 mL
   4 L 500 mL – 1 L 340 mL = 3 L 160 mL
   The total volume of water that both
   containers can hold is **3 L 160 mL**.
2. Amount of water when the tank is half
   filled = 83 gal – 29 gal = 54 gal
   Capacity of the tank = 2 × 54 gal = 108 gal
   The capacity of the tank is **108 gal**.
3. 3 L 450 mL + 4 L 570 mL = 7 L 1,020 mL
                          = 8 L 20 mL
   Paul and Mary add 8 L 20 mL of water
   into the container.
   10 L – 8 L 20 mL = 9 L 1,000 mL – 8 L 20 mL
                    = 1 L 980 mL
   The container can hold **1 L 980 mL** more
   water.
4.

   4 × 3 pt = 12 pt
   Jug B has 12 pt of water.
   3 qt = 3 × 2 pt = 6 pt
   12 pt + 6 pt = 18 pt
   Jug C has 18 pt of water.
   18 pt = 9 qt
         = 2 gal 1 qt
   The volume of water in Jug C is **2 gal 1 qt**.
5. 370 mL + 290 mL + 8 L 450 mL = 9 L 110 mL
   Oliver makes **9 L 110 mL** of punch in all.
6. 3 L 485 mL + 2 L 108 mL – 93 mL
   = 5 L 500 mL
   The capacity of the pail is **5 L 500 mL**.

Challenging Problems (pp. 67–70)

1. 1 container + 2 bottles = 920 mL
   2 containers + 1 bottle = 850 mL
   3 containers + 3 bottles
   = 920 mL + 850 mL = 1,770 mL
   1 container + 1 bottle
   = 1,770 mL ÷ 3 = 590 mL
   850 mL – 590 mL = 850 mL – 600 mL + 10 mL
   = 250 mL + 10 mL
   = 260 mL

   (a) The capacity of one plastic container
   is **260 mL**.

   (b) 590 mL – 260 mL = 330 mL
   The capacity of one bottle is **330 mL**.

2. (a)

3 L	7 L
0	7
3	4
0	4
3	1

   (b)

3 L	7 L		3 L	7 L
3	0	or	0	7
0	3		3	4
3	3		0	4
0	6		3	1
3	6		0	1
2	7		1	0
2	0		1	7
0	2		3	5
3	2			
0	5			

3. (a)
   David: 100 mL   Ruth: 120 mL

Number of cups	Volume of water
1	100
2	200
3	300
4	400
5	500
6	(600)

Number of cups	Volume of water
1	120
2	240
3	360
4	480
5	(600)

   David poured **6** cups of water and
   Ruth poured **5** cups of water into the
   pail.

   (b) 600 mL + 600 mL = 1 L 200 mL
   The total volume of water that was
   poured into the pail was **1 L 200 mL**.

4. Amount of liquid X required to make 2 L
   of soup = 2 L ÷ 2 = 1 L = 1,000 mL
   Number of cans required
   = 1,000 mL ÷ 100 mL = 10
   She must buy **10** cans of liquid X to
   prepare 2 L of soup.

5. 4 × 2 qt = 8 qt
   4 jugs have a capacity of 8 qt.
   50 gal – 8 qt = 50 × 4 qt – 8 qt
   = 200 qt – 8 qt
   = 192 qt
   4 buckets have a capacity of 192 qt.
   192 ÷ 4 = 48
   1 bucket has a capacity of 48 qt.
   3 buckets have a capacity of 3 × 48
   = 144 qt
   = 144 ÷ 4 gal
   = 36 gal
   The capacity of 3 buckets is **36 gal**.

6. $\frac{1}{2}$ jug has the same capacity as 5
   glasses.
   1 jug has the same capacity as 2 × 5
   = 10 glasses.
   4 jugs have the same capacity as 4 × 10
   = 40 glasses.
   1 glass has a capacity of 250 mL.
   40 glasses have a capacity of 40 × 250 mL
   = 10,000 mL
   = 10 L
   The capacity of 4 jugs is **10 L**.

7.

3 L	5 L	8 L
0	5	0
3	0	2
0	5	2
3	0	4

8.

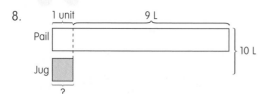

2 units = 10 L − 9 L = 1 L = 1,000 mL
1 unit = 1,000 mL ÷ 2 = 500 mL
Capacity of the jug = 500 mL
The capacity of the jug is **500 mL**.

Note: A common mistake is to claim that the
capacity of the jug is
10 L − 9 L = 1 L = 1,000 mL
If the jug has a capacity 1 L, then the pail
has capacity 10 L − 1 L = 9 L, which is
8 L more than that of the jug. Thus, the
capacity of the jug cannot be 1 L.

9.

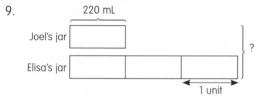

1 unit = 220 mL
4 units = 4 × 220 mL = 880 mL
The total volume of water in both jars is
880 mL.

10.

5 L	9 L	Container
0	0	12
5	0	7
0	5	7
5	5	2
1	9	2
1	0	11
0	1	11
5	1	6
0	6	6

7 Money

Practice Questions (pp. 74-77)

1. $18.70 + $33.40 + $52.10
   = $104.20
   All three have **$104.20** in total.
   Estimated answer:
   $19 + $33 + $52
   = $20 + $32 + $52 = $104

2. $100 − $22.90 − $42.50 = $34.60
   Matthew received **$34.60**.
   Estimated answer:
   $23 + $42 = $65
   $100 − $65 = $35

3. $28 ÷ 2 = $14
   Each shared $14.
   $14 − $5.60 = $8.40
   He had **$8.40** left.

4. 5 × $3 = $15
   Mary spent $15 on the books.
   $15 + $8.50 = **$23.50**
   She had $23.50 at first.

5. $51.35 − $23.80 − $23.80 = $3.75
   Irene saves **$3.75** more than Jenny.
   Estimated answer:
   $51 − $24 = $50 − $23
             = $27
   $27 − $24 = $3

6. 5 × $1 + 2 × $10 = $5 + $20 = $25
   Joshua's godfather gave him $25.
   $27.35 − $25 = $2.35
   He needs **$2.35** more.

7. *Before*

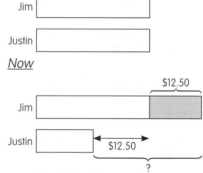

   $12.50 + $12.50
   = $12 + $12 + $0.50 + $0.50
   = $24 + $1
   = $25
   Jim has **$25** more than Justin now.

8. $95 − $35 = $60
   She needs $60 more to buy the dress.
   $60 ÷ $5 = 12
   Jennifer must save for **12** weeks before
   she can buy the dress.

9.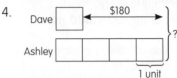

2 units = $137 − $29
= $138 − $30
= $108
1 unit = $108 ÷ 2 = $54
1 unit + $29 = $54 + $29
= $53 + $30
= $83
Roy has **$54** and June has **$83**.

10. (a) 2 × 10¢ + 22¢
Two 10¢ stamps + one 22¢ stamp
= 3 stamps
The least number of stamps for
Package 1 would be **3**.

(b) 10¢ + 3 × 22¢
One 10¢ stamp + three 22¢ stamps
= 4 stamps
The least number of stamps for
Package 2 would be **4**.

(c) 2 × 22¢ + 50¢
Two 22¢ stamps + one 50¢ stamp
= 3 stamps
The least number of stamps for
Package 3 would be **3**.

Challenging Problems (pp. 81-84)

1. $1.20 = 120¢; $4.80 = 480¢
120¢ − 80¢ = 40¢
He earns 40¢ for every fish he sells.
480¢ ÷ 40¢ = 12
He must sell **12** fish in order to earn $4.80.

2.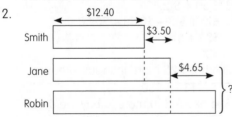

$12.40 + $3.50 = $15.90
Jane has $15.90.
$15.90 + $4.65 = $20.55
Robin has $20.55.
$15.90 + $20.55 = $36.45
Robin and Jane have **$36.45** altogether.

3. Mr. Tan:
1 apple costs 40¢
5 apples cost 5 × 40¢ = 200¢
= $2
Mr. Yang: 5 apples cost $1.80
$2.00 − $1.80 = $0.20 = 20¢
**I should buy from Mr. Yang because his
apples are cheaper by 20¢.**

4.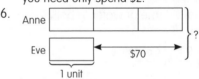

3 units = $180
1 unit = $180 ÷ 3 = $60
5 units = 5 × $60 = $300
They have **$300** in total.

5. Assume the worst case:
The first 3 balls obtained are of different
colors.
The 4th ball will match any of the 3 colors.
The least amount of money that I need to
spend is **$4**.
Note: The best case arises when the first 2
balls are of the same color. In other words,
you need only spend $2.

6.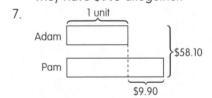

2 units = $70
4 units = $70 × 2 = $140
They have **$140** altogether.

7.
Adam
Pam
$58.10
$9.90
1 unit

2 units = $58.10 − $9.90
= $58.20 − $10.00
= $48.20
1 unit = $48.20 ÷ 2 = $24.10
1 unit + $9.90 = $24.10 + $9.90 = $34
Adam has **$24.10** and Pam has **$34**.

8. _Method 1_
$15.30 = 1,530¢
1,530¢ ÷ 9 = 170¢
$2 = 200¢
200¢ − 170¢ = 30¢
He makes **30¢** profit on each badge.

Method 2

He sold 9 badges for $9 \times \$2 = \$18$.
Profit he made on 9 badges
$= \$18 - \$15.30 = \$2.70$
Profit he made on each badge
$= \$2.70 \div 9 = \$0.30 = 30¢$
He makes **30¢** on each badge.

9. Amount Henry spent for the
2 items $= 2 \times \$10 - \$2.40 = \$17.60$
Look for 2 items whose costs sum up to
$17.60.
$\$17.60 = \$9.50$ (shorts) $+ \$8.10$ (jacket)
Henry bought **a pair of shorts** and **a jacket**.

10. *Method 1*

$$\begin{array}{rl} 1 \text{ pear} + 2 \text{ oranges} & = \$1.00 \\ 2 \text{ pears} + 1 \text{ orange} & = \$1.10 \\ \hline 3 \text{ pears} + 3 \text{ oranges} & = \$2.10 \end{array}$$

1 pear + 1 orange $= \$2.10 \div 3 = \$0.70$
2 pears + 2 oranges $= 2 \times \$0.70 = \$1.40$
The total cost of 2 pears and 2 oranges
is **$1.40**.

Method 2

1 pear + 2 oranges $= \$1.00$
2 pears + 4 oranges $= 2 \times \$1.00 = \$2.00$
Given: 2 pears + 1 orange $= \$1.10$
So, 3 oranges cost $\$2.00 - \$1.10 = \$0.90$.
1 orange costs $\$0.90 \div 3 = \$0.30 = 30¢$
2 oranges cost $2 \times 30¢ = 60¢$
So, 1 pear costs $\$1.00 - 60¢ = 40¢$.
2 pears cost $2 \times 40¢ = 80¢$
Total cost of 2 pears and 2 oranges
$= 80¢ + 60¢ = 140¢ = \$1.40$
The total cost of 2 pears and 2 oranges
is **$1.40**.
Note: In Method 1, there is no need to know
the price of each fruit. In Method 2, the price
of each fruit is needed.

8　Fractions

Practice Questions (pp. 88-89)

1. $12 - 3 = 9$
9 marbles are left.
Fraction of marbles left $= \dfrac{9}{12} = \dfrac{3}{4}$
$\dfrac{3}{4}$ of the marbles was left.

2. $18 - 6 = 12$
12 stuffed toys were left.
Fraction of the stuffed toys that were left
$= \dfrac{12}{18} = \dfrac{2}{3}$
$\dfrac{2}{3}$ of the stuffed toys were left.

3. 1 whole has 4 quarters.
9 wholes have $9 \times 4 = 36$ quarters.
There are **36** quarters in 9 wholes.

4. There are 12 identical rectangles.
6 halves = 3 wholes
3 rectangles are shaded.
Fraction of the figure that is shaded $= \dfrac{3}{12}$
$= \dfrac{1}{4}$
$\dfrac{1}{4}$ of the figure is shaded.

5. *Method 1*

$$\dfrac{6}{9} = \dfrac{3 \times 2}{3 \times 3} = \dfrac{2}{3}$$

$$\dfrac{2}{3} = \dfrac{2 \times 2}{3 \times 2} = \dfrac{4}{6}$$

$\square = \mathbf{6}$

Method 2

$$\dfrac{6}{9} = \dfrac{4}{\square}$$

$6 \times \square = 9 \times 4 = 36$
$\square = 36 \div 6 = \mathbf{6}$

6. The figure is made up of 10 rectangles.

$$\dfrac{3}{5} = \dfrac{6}{10}$$

Any 6 shaded rectangles would
represent $\dfrac{3}{5}$ of the figure.

7. $\dfrac{1}{2} = \dfrac{1 \times 6}{2 \times 6} = \dfrac{6}{12}$

$\dfrac{5}{6} = \dfrac{5 \times 2}{6 \times 2} = \dfrac{10}{12}$

$\dfrac{3}{4} = \dfrac{3 \times 3}{4 \times 3} = \dfrac{9}{12}$

Beginning from the smallest, we have $\dfrac{1}{2}$,
$\dfrac{3}{4}, \dfrac{5}{6}$.

Challenging Problems (pp. 93-96)

1. (a) 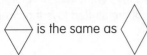 is the same as

   (b) Two sixths is the same as one third.

   (c) $\dfrac{2}{6} = \dfrac{1}{3}$

   or

   (a) 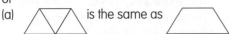 is the same as

   (b) Three sixths is the same as one half.

   (c) $\dfrac{3}{6} = \dfrac{1}{2}$

2. (a) $\dfrac{1}{8} + \dfrac{1}{8} = \dfrac{1}{4}$

   (b) $\dfrac{1}{6} + \dfrac{1}{6} + \dfrac{1}{6} = \dfrac{1}{2}$

3. $\dfrac{3}{6}$ represents 18.

   $\dfrac{1}{6}$ represents $\dfrac{1}{3} \times 18 = 6$.

   The number is **6**.

4. $\dfrac{1}{2} = \dfrac{4}{8} = \dfrac{1}{\boxed{8}} + \dfrac{1}{\boxed{8}} + \dfrac{1}{\boxed{8}} + \dfrac{1}{\boxed{8}}$

5. (a) Look for pairs of fractions that add up to $\dfrac{7}{10}$.

   For example, $\dfrac{1}{10}$ and $\dfrac{6}{10}$, $\dfrac{2}{10}$ and $\dfrac{5}{10}$, $\dfrac{3}{10}$ and $\dfrac{4}{10}$.

   (b) Look for pairs of fractions whose difference is $\dfrac{3}{10}$.

   For example, $\dfrac{10}{10}$ and $\dfrac{7}{10}$

$\dfrac{7}{10}$ and $\dfrac{4}{10}$	$\dfrac{4}{10}$ and $\dfrac{1}{10}$
$\dfrac{9}{10}$ and $\dfrac{6}{10}$	$\dfrac{6}{10}$ and $\dfrac{3}{10}$
$\dfrac{8}{10}$ and $\dfrac{5}{10}$	$\dfrac{5}{10}$ and $\dfrac{2}{10}$

6.

   blue green

   $\dfrac{1}{4}$ of 4 remaining parts represent 1 part.

   3 out of 5 parts were not painted.

   $\dfrac{3}{5}$ of the rod was not painted.

7.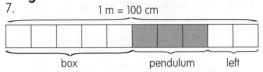

   1 m = 100 cm

   box   pendulum   left

   $\dfrac{2}{10}$ of the string was left.

   $\dfrac{1}{10}$ of the string is 10 cm.

   $\dfrac{2}{10}$ of the string is 20 cm.

   20 cm of the string was left.

8.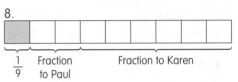

   $\dfrac{1}{9}$ Fraction   Fraction to Karen
        to Paul

   (a) $\dfrac{1}{4}$ of 8 remaining parts represent 2 parts.

   $\dfrac{2}{9}$ of Oliver's stickers were given to Paul.

   (b) 6 out of 9 parts were given to Karen.

   $\dfrac{6}{9} = \dfrac{3 \times 2}{3 \times 3} = \dfrac{2}{3}$

   $\dfrac{2}{3}$ of Oliver's stickers were given to Karen.

9 Time

Practice Questions (pp. 100-102)

1.

8:15 P.M. $\xrightarrow{\text{+ 45 min}}$ 9:00 P.M. $\xrightarrow{\text{+ 1 h}}$ 10:00 P.M.

1 h + 45 min = 1 h 45 min
The movie lasted **1 h 45 min**.

2.

11:35 A.M. $\xrightarrow{\text{+ 25 min}}$ 12:00 P.M. $\xrightarrow{\text{+ 15 min}}$ 12:15 P.M.

25 min + 15 min = 40 min.
She was teaching for **40 min**.

3.

8:30 A.M. $\xrightarrow{\text{3 h 30 min}}$ 12:00 noon $\xrightarrow{\text{+ 6 h}}$ 6:00 P.M.

6 h + 3 h 30 min = 9 h 30 min
The opening hours last for **9 h 30 min**.

4. 80 min = 1 h 20 min

8:15 P.M. $\xrightarrow{\text{– 1 h}}$ 7.15 P.M. $\xrightarrow{\text{– 15 min}}$

7:00 P.M. $\xrightarrow{\text{– 5 min}}$ 6:55 P.M.

The movie started at **6:55 P.M.**

5.

Mon	Tue	Wed	Thu	Fri	Sat	Sun
Yesterday	Today	Tomorrow	1 day after tomorrow	2 days after tomorrow	3 days after tomorrow	4 days after tomorrow

From the time line, 4 days after tomorrow is **Sunday**.

6. *Method 1*

9:40 P.M. $\xrightarrow{\text{4 h}}$ 1:40 A.M.

$\downarrow$ 20 min

2:15 A.M. $\xleftarrow{}$ 2:00 A.M.
15 min

4 h = 4 × 60 min = 240 min
Number of minutes
= 240 minutes + 20 minutes + 15 minutes
= 275 minutes
There are **275 minutes** between the two times.

Method 2

9:40 P.M. $\xrightarrow{\text{+ 20 min}}$ 10:00 P.M.

$\downarrow$ + 2 h

2:15 A.M. $\xleftarrow{}$ 12 midnight
2 h 15 min

20 min + 2 h + 2 h 15 min = 4 h 35 min
4 h × 60 = 240 min
240 min + 35 min = 275 min
There are **275 minutes** between the two times.

7.

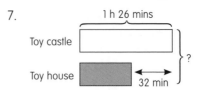

Toy castle

Toy house   32 min

1 h 26 min + 1 h 26 min = 2 h 52 min
2 h 52 min – 32 min = 2 h 20 min
Henry took **2 h 20 min** to build a toy house and a toy castle altogether.

8.

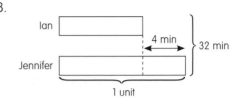

Ian   4 min   32 min

Jennifer

1 unit

2 units = 32 min + 4 min = 36 min
1 unit = 36 min ÷ 2 = 18 min
Jennifer jogged for **18 minutes**.

9. From May 18 to May 31, there are 31 – 18 + 1 = 14 days.
From June 1 to June 17, there are 17 days.
14 + 17 = 31
There are **31 days** from May 18 to June 17.

Challenging Problems (pp. 106-109)

1.

3 days after 3 days before yesterday

Tue	Wed	Thu	Fri	Sat	Sun
3 days before yesterday	2 days before yesterday	1 day before yesterday	Yesterday	Today	Tomorrow

3 days after 3 days before yesterday is **Friday**.

2. 6 pieces need 5 sawings.
11 pieces need 10 sawings.
5 sawings take 60 minutes.
1 sawing takes 60 ÷ 5 = 12 minutes.
10 sawings will take 10 × 12 min
= 120 min = 2 h.
It will take the carpenter **2 h** to saw the piece of wood into 11 pieces.

3. From 8:00 A.M. on Sunday to 8:00 A.M. on Monday, there are 24 hours.

In 1 hour, the clock loses 5 minutes.
In 24 hours, the clock will lose 24 × 5 min
= 12 × 10 min
= 120 min
= 2 h

8:00 A.M. $\xrightarrow{\text{– 2 h}}$ 6:00 A.M.

The clock will show **6:00 A.M.** at 8:00 A.M. on Monday.

4. (a) The digits of each individual date add up to 4. For example 0 + 4 = 4, 1 + 3 = 4 …
    The sum of the digits equal to 4 fall on the **4th, 13th, 22nd, 31st** of a month.
    (b) Least number of times = **3**;
    Most number of times = **4**

5.

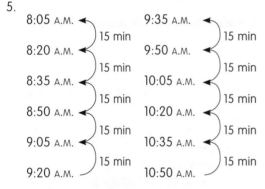

There are 12 different times at 15-minute intervals between 8:00 A.M. and 11:00 A.M.
There are **12** buses between 8:00 A.M. and 11:00 A.M.

6. From 5 P.M. to 9 P.M., there are 4 hours.
    In 1 h, the watch is 5 min faster.
    In 4 h, the watch is 4 × 5 = 20 min faster.
    9:00 P.M. – 20 min = 8:40 P.M.
    When Tom's watch shows 9:00 P.M., the correct time is **8:40 P.M.**

7.

Sally's age	Sally's cousin's age
12	21
13	22
14	23
15	24
16	25
17	26
18	27
19	28
20	29
21	30
22	31
23	32

23 – 12 = 11 or 32 – 21 = 11
This will happen again in **11** years' time.

8. From 9:25 P.M. on Wednesday to 9:25 P.M. on Thursday, there are 24 hours.
    3 h – 25 min = 2 h 35 min
    (or 9:25 P.M. $\xrightarrow{\text{+ 35 min}}$ 10:00 P.M. $\xrightarrow{\text{+ 2 h}}$ midnight)

    From midnight on Thursday to 1:19 A.M. on Friday, there are 1 h 19 min.

    midnight $\xrightarrow{\text{+ 1 h 19 min}}$ 1:19 A.M.
    24 h + 2 h 35 min + 1 h 19 min
    = 27 h + 35 min + 19 min
    = 27 × 60 min + 54 min
    = 1,620 min + 54 min
    = 1,674 min
    There are **1,674 minutes** between 9:25 P.M. on Wednesday and 1:19 A.M. on Friday.

9.

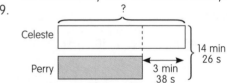

14 min 26 s + 3 min 38 s
= 17 min + 4 s + 22 s + 38 s
= 18 min + 4 s
18 min 4 s ÷ 2 = 9 min 2 s
Celeste cycled for **9 minutes 2 seconds**.

10. (a) Singapore time
        = Geneva time + 7 h
        The time difference is **7 h**.
    (b) Sydney time
        = Singapore time + 3 h
        The time difference is **3 h**.
    (c) 6:10 A.M. $\xrightarrow{\text{– 7 h}}$ 11:10 P.M.
        It is **11:10 P.M.** in Geneva.
    (d) 10:25 A.M. $\xrightarrow{\text{– 3 h}}$ 7:25 A.M.
        It is **7:25 A.M.** in Singapore.

10   Data Analysis

Practice Questions (pp. 118-123)

1. (a) The most popular subject is represented by the longest bar, which is **Science**.
   (b) **2** more students prefer English to History.
   (c) Total number of students
   = 8 + 12 + 10 + 13 = 43
   The total number of students in the class is **43**.

2. 50 + 70 + 30 = 150
   150 like red, blue, and purple.
   150 ÷ 5 = 30
   30 students like purple.

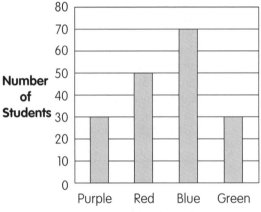

Favorite Color

3. (a) **35** students liked yellow.
   (b) **Blue** was the most popular color.
   (c) 40 students liked red.
   30 students liked pink.
   40 − 30 = 10
   10 more students preferred red to pink.

4. (a) 12 + 15 + 6 = 33
   33 adults preferred to travel by bus, car, or van in all.
   (b) Van: 6, Bus: 12
   6 + 12 = 18
   Train: 10, Bicycle: 8
   10 + 8 = 18
   There were as many adults who traveled by van and by bus as those who traveled by **train** and by **bicycle**.
   (c) 15 − 8 = 7
   7 more adults traveled by car than by bicycle.

(d) 15 − 6 = 9
   The difference between the number of adults who chose the most popular and the least popular mode of transport is **9** adults.

5. (a) The most popular hobby is represented by the longest bar, which is **online games**.
   (b) **500** teenagers liked to play guitar.
   (c) 600 − 150 = 450
   450 more teenagers prefer photography to dancing.
   (d) 350 + 150 = 500
   500 teenagers like soccer or dancing altogether.
   (e) 700 − 150 = 550
   550 fewer teenagers like dancing than online games.

6. (a)

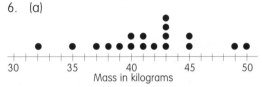

Mass in kilograms

(b) We look for the students with mass greater than 38 kg and less than 42 kg.
   There were **5** students in total.
   (c) We look for the students with mass greater than 40 kg.
   There were **11** students in total.
   (d) We look for the students with mass less than 38 kg.
   There were **3** students in total.
   (e) From the line plot, the most number of students appear in the column "43."
   The most common mass was **43 kg**.

7. (a) We look at the question numbers on the line plot.
   There were **10** quiz questions.
   (b) We look for questions with no ●'s for questions all students got correct.
   All students answered **2** questions correctly: questions 1 and 4.
   (c) From the line plot, the most number of students appear in the column "10."
   The most difficult question for most students was question **10**.
   (d) There are 8 ●'s under the question number 9.

Now,

$$\frac{\text{number of students who got question 9 wrong}}{\text{number of students}} = \frac{8}{14} = \frac{4}{7}$$

$\frac{4}{7}$ of the students got question 9 wrong.

(e) There are 6 ●'s under the question number 7.

$14 - 6 = 8$

8 students got question 7 correct.

$$\frac{\text{Number of students who got question 7 correct}}{\text{Number of students}} = \frac{8}{14} = \frac{4}{7}$$

$\frac{4}{7}$ of the students got question 7 correct.

Challenging Problems (pp. 129-133)

1. (a) $40 + 35 + 55 = 130$
   130 souvenirs were distributed from Tuesday to Thursday.
   (b) $130 + 20 + 50 + 15 = 215$
   215 souvenirs were prepared for the week.

2. (a) From the bar graph, the longest bar is the one representing Ian.
   Ian took the longest time and thus was the slowest swimmer.
   (b) From the bar graph, the shortest bar is the one representing Claire.
   Claire took the shortest time and thus was the fastest swimmer.
   (c) From the bar graph, the second longest bar is the one representing Paul.
   Paul was the second last swimmer.
   (d) From the bar graph, the third shortest bar is the one representing Bob.
   Bob came in third.

3. (a)

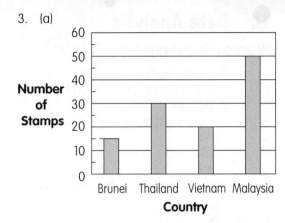

(b) (i) Arthur has the most number of **Malaysia** stamps.
   (ii) He has the least number of **Brunei** stamps.
   (iii) Malaysia: 50; Brunei: 15
   $50 - 15 = 35$
   Arthur has **35** more Malaysia stamps than Brunei stamps.
   (iv) Brunei: 15; Thailand: 30, Vietnam: 20; Malaysia: 50
   $15 + 30 + 20 + 50 = 115$
   Arthur has **115** stamps altogether.

4. (a)

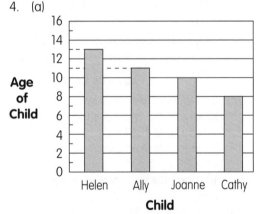

(b) (i) Helen: 13; Cathy: 8
   $13 + 8 = 21$
   The total age of Helen and Cathy is **21** years old.
   (ii) Number of years for Joanne to reach Helen's age
   $= 13 - 10 = 3$
   $11 + 3 = 14$
   Ally will be **14** years old.
   (iii) Number of years for Cathy to reach Joanne's age
   $= 10 - 8 = 2$
   $13 + 2 = 15$
   Helen will be **15** years old.

5.

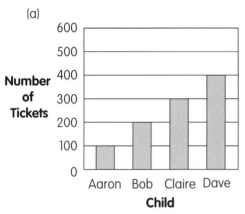

10 units = 1,000
1 unit = 100
2 units = 200
4 units = 400
3 units = 300

(a)

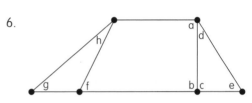

Number of Tickets |

600
500
400
300
200
100
0

Aaron   Bob   Claire   Dave
Child

(b) (i) From the bar graph, the shortest bar is the one representing Aaron. **Aaron** sold the least number of tickets.
   (ii) From the bar graph, the longest bar is the one representing Dave. **Dave** sold the most number of tickets.
   (iii) Number of tickets that Bob would have to sell
   = 300 − 200 = 100
   Bob would have to sell **100** more tickets in order to match the number of tickets sold by Claire.

11   Geometry

Practice Questions (pp. 137-138)

1. There are **3** right angles.
2. (a) There are **2** angles smaller than a right angle.
   (b) There are **2** angles greater than a right angle.

3.

	Angle
Right angle	b, d, g
Smaller than a right angle	a, f
Greater than a right angle	c, e

4. (a) There are **0** right angles.
   (b) There is **1** angle smaller than a right angle.
   (c) There are **4** angles greater than a right angle.

5.

6.

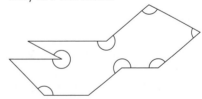

(a) a, b, c
   3 angles are right angles.
(b) d, e, f, g, h
   5 angles are smaller than a right angle.

Challenging Problems (pp. 140-143)

1. (a) Any two of the following: **A, D, G**
   (b) Any three of the following: **A, C, E, F, G, H**
   (c) **B**
   (d) **F**
2. They are the same.
3.

[diagram]

7 angle measures are greater than a right angle.

4. The greatest number of right angles that a six-sided figure can have is **5**.

5. (a) There are **16** right angles.
   (b) There are **7** right angles.

6. a, b, c, d, e, f
   6 angle measures smaller than a right angle can be formed.

   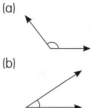

7. Answers vary. An example is:
   (a)

   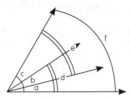

   (b)

8. $\frac{1}{4}$ of a turn is a right angle.

12 Area and Perimeter

Practice Questions (pp. 147-149)

1. Area = length × width
   = 18 cm × 6 cm
   = 108 cm²
   Perimeter = 18 cm + 6 cm + 18 cm + 6 cm
   = 48 cm
   Its perimeter is **48 cm** and its area is **108 cm²**.

2. Perimeter of enclosure
   = 2 × (length + width)
   = 2 × (50 m + 35 m)
   = **170 m**
   One meter of fencing cost $9.
   170 meters of fencing cost 170 × $9
   = $1,530.
   It costs **$1,530** to fence the enclosure.
   Area of enclosure = 50 m × 35 m
   = **1,750** square meters.

3. Perimeter
   = length + width + length + width
   = 175 m + 80 m + 175 m + 80 m
   = 510 m
   Total distance that Henry ran
   = 3 × Perimeter of field
   = 3 × 510 m
   = 1,530 m
   He ran a total distance of **1,530 m**.

4. Length of rectangular piece of cardboard
   = 3 × width
   = 3 × 25 cm
   = 75 cm
   Perimeter
   = length + width + length + width
   = 75 cm + 25 cm + 75 cm + 25 cm
   = 200 cm
   Its perimeter is **200 cm**.

5. 10 cm + 7 cm + 8 cm + 5 cm + 6 cm
   = 36 cm
   The perimeter of the figure is **36 cm**.

6. Length of wire
   = Perimeter of rectangle
   = length + width + length + width
   = 12 cm + 9 cm + 12 cm + 9 cm
   = 42 cm
   The length of the wire is **42 cm**.

7. Length of wire used = 75 cm – 3 cm
   = 72 cm
   Perimeter of square = Length of wire used
   = 72 cm
   = 4 × 18 cm
   The length of the square is **18 cm**.

8. Area of figure A = 8 square units
   Area of figure B = 5 square units
   Area of figure C = 9 square units
   Perimeter of figure A = 12 units
   Perimeter of figure B = 12 units
   Perimeter of figure C = 12 units
   These figures have the **same perimeter**.

Challenging Problems (pp. 153-156)

1. (a) 6 cm + 8 cm + 6 cm + 8 cm = 28 cm
   Its perimeter is **28 cm**.
   Note: The dimensions 3 cm and 4 cm are not needed in the computation

   Area of A = 6 cm × 5 cm
   = 30 cm²
   Area of B = 3 cm × 4 cm
   = 12 cm²
   Total Area = 30 cm² + 12 cm²
   = 42 cm²
   Its area is **42 cm²**.

(b) 6 cm + 6 cm + 6 cm + 6 cm = 24 cm
Its perimeter is **24 cm**.

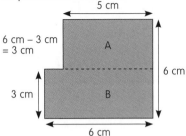

Area of A = 5 cm × 3 cm
= 15 cm^2
Area of B = 6 cm × 3 cm
= 18 cm^2
Total Area = 15 cm^2 + 18 cm^2
= 33 cm^2
Its area is **33 cm²**.

2. (a) 6 cm + 8 cm + 6 cm + 8 cm = 28 cm
Its perimeter is **28 cm**.
Note: The dimensions 2.2 cm and 5 cm
are not needed in the computation

(b) Shift the lines, as shown by the
arrows.
They form a rectangle of length 6 cm
and width 5 cm.

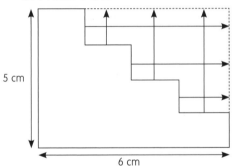

5 cm + 6 cm + 5 cm + 6 cm = 22 cm
Its perimeter is **22 cm**.

3. Observe that cutting off the four corners
does not affect the perimeter.
The perimeter of the cross is equal to the
perimeter of the original square.
Perimeter of the new figure
= Perimeter of the square
= 4 × 12 cm
= 48 cm
The perimeter of the new figure is **48 cm**.

4.
8 m

24 m

24 m

Number of orange trees = 12
Number of oranges = 12 × 100
= 1,200
He will get **1,200** oranges from his
orchard.

5. The figure is made up of 12 equal sides.
Perimeter of the figure
= 12 × 6 cm
= 72 cm
Its perimeter is **72 cm**.

6. Let the length of one rectangle be 3 units.
Length of the square = 3 units
Width of the rectangle = 1 unit
Perimeter of the rectangle
= 3 units + 1 unit + 3 units + 1 unit
= 8 units
8 units = 16 cm
1 unit = 2 cm
3 units = 6 cm
Length of the square = 6 cm
Perimeter of the square
= 4 × 6 cm = 24 cm
The perimeter of the square is **24 cm**.

13   Review Questions 1

Practice Questions (pp. 159-162)

1.
Large jug		

Small jug								

2 × 5 = 10
A large jug full of water can fill **10** cups.

2.

10:00 A.M. ——12 h——→ 10:00 P.M.

9:30 P.M. ——30 min——→ 10:00 P.M.
12 h − 30 min = 11 h 30 min
The shop is open for **11 h 30 min** each
day.

3. (a) Out of all the digits (0, 1, 2 ,…, 9), 9 is the largest.
Therefore the largest three-digit number is **999**.

(b) Out of all the digits (0, 1, 2,…, 9), 0 is the smallest.
Since it has to be a four-digit number, the first digit cannot be 0.
The next smallest digit is 1. 1 is the first digit and the last three digits are 0.
Therefore the smallest four-digit number is **1,000**.

4. $17.50 – $2.50 = $15
The 5 DVDs cost $15.
$15 ÷ 5 = $3
1 DVD cost **$3.00**.

5. _Method 1_

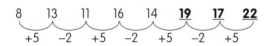

Method 2

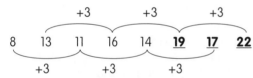

6. Odd digits: 1, 3, 5, 7, 9
Let abc be the 3-digit odd number.

a   b   c
↑   ↑
hundreds digit   tens digit

If a = 1, then b = 2 and c = 10 – 1 – 2 = 7
The number is 127, an odd number.
If a = 2, then b = 4, c = 10 – 2 – 4 = 4
But 244 is not an odd number.
If a = 3, then b = 6, c = 10 – 3 – 6 = 1
361 is an odd number.
The number I am thinking could be **127** or **361**.

7. _Method 1_
72 cm ÷ 3 = 24 cm
24 cm ÷ 3 = 8 cm
The length of one side of a triangle is **8 cm**.

Method 2
3 triangles have 9 equal sides.
72 cm ÷ 9 = 8 cm
The length of one side of a triangle is **8 cm**.

8.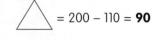
110

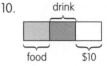 = 200 – 110 = **90**

 = 110

□ = 110 – 90 = **20**

9. The area of the figure is **12** square units.

10.

drink

food $10

1 unit = $10
3 units = 3 × $10 = $30
Amount of pocket money = $30
Her pocket money was **$30**.

Challenging Problems (pp. 165-168)

1. 3 llamas in front

2 llamas between

3 llamas behind

The fewest number of llamas is **4**.

2. Digit "1" in the ones place: 1, 11, 21, … , 91 — 10 times
Digit "1" in the tens place: 10, 11, 12 … , 19 — 10 times
Digit "1" in the hundreds place: 100 — 1 time
10 + 10 + 1 = 21
The digit "1" appears **21** times in numbers from 1 to 100.

3. The teddy bear costs ($9.90 + $6.35).
$9.90 + $9.90 + $6.35 + $2.20 = $28.35
She had **$28.35** at first.

4. 35 + 1 + 42 = 78
There were **78** people in the line.

5.

6. 5 years ago, Alfred was 11 years old.
Now, Alfred is 11 + 5 = 16 years old.
16 − 6 = 10
Alfred's sister is **10** years old now.

7. (a) 15 × 3 oz = 45 oz
9 × 5 oz = 45 oz
45 oz + 45 oz = 90 oz
They bought **90 oz** of snacks in total.

(b) Make use of the multiples of 3 oz
and 5 oz to find out.
Numbers divisible by 3: 3, 6, 9, 12,
15, 18, 21…
Numbers divisible by 5: 5, 10, 15,
20…
Theresa's snacks weighed 5 oz and
is divisible by 20.
(i) **Theresa** dropped her snacks.
(ii) 20 oz ÷ 5 oz = 4
4 packs were dropped.

8. RRBG

Green	Blue	Red
1	1	2
5	5	10

5 + 5 + 10 = 20
Rose used **20** beads altogether.

9. 2 × $6.50 + 3 × $4.00 = $13 + $12 = $25
5 kilogram of grade C flour cost $25.
$25 ÷ 5 = $5
1 kilogram of grade C flour costs **$5**.

10. Suppose there were 13 bicycles.
Then there would be a total of 13 × 2
= 26 wheels.
The difference of 44 − 26 = 18 wheels
must have come from the cars.
1 car has 2 more wheels than 1 bicycle.
Thus, there are 18 ÷ 2 = 9 cars, and
13 − 9 = 4 bicycles.
There were **9** cars in the parking lot.

11. Answers vary. Two examples are:

14 Review Questions 2

Practice Questions (pp. 171-174)

1. (a) **21** = 8 + 13
34 = 13 + 21
(b) **25** = 5 × 5
36 = 6 × 6

2. (a) $\frac{1}{2}$

(b) $\frac{3}{8}$

(c) $\frac{1}{4}$

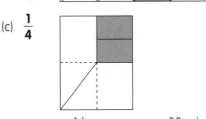

3.
5:30 P.M. $\xrightarrow{-1\,h}$ 4:30 P.M. $\xrightarrow{-30\,min}$
4:00 P.M. $\xrightarrow{-5\,min}$ 3:55 P.M.
He left his school at **3:55 P.M.**

4. 13 + 1 + 13 = 27
27 students took the test.

5.
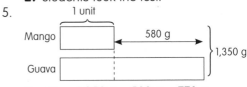

2 units = 1,350 g − 580 g = 770 g
1 unit = 770 g ÷ 2 = 385 g
The mass of the mango is **385 g**.

6. The tennis ball is the biggest while the
marble is the smallest.
The bigger the ball is, the more space it
will occupy.
(a) The **box with tennis balls** has the
least number of balls.
(b) The **box with marbles** has the most
number of balls.

7. *Method 1*
4 + 3 + 2 + 1 = 10
10 handshakes took place among the 5
friends.
Method 2
The 5 persons each shake hands with
the other 4. So there are a total of 5 × 4
= 20 handshakes. But each of these 20
handshakes is counted twice.
Hence, there are 20 ÷ 2 = 10 handshakes
that took place among the 5 friends.
10 handshakes took place among the 5
friends.

8. (a) 1,200 − 240 = 960
      960 ÷ 8 = 120
      There were **120** bags of apples
      altogether.
   (b) 120 × $3 = $360
      He collected **$360**.
9. 18 square units is for 1 part.
   Area of the shaded part is half of 1 part.
   18 ÷ 2 = 9
   The area of the shaded part is **9 square units**.
10. **Dennis, Esther, Aaron, Cathy, Betty**

Challenging Problems (pp. 176-180)

1. 4,054 + 128 − 3,656 = 526
   There were **526** parents.
2. 1 + 2 + 3 + 4 + 5 + 6
   = (1 + 6) + (2 + 5) + (3 + 4)
   = 3 × 7
   = 21
   All the dots on the 6 sides of the die sum
   up to 21.
   21 − 16 = 5
   The number of dots on the face resting
   on the table is **5**.
3. A + A = A or 1A
   A can only be 0.
   ```
     B 0
   + B 0
   ─────
   1 0 0
   ```
   So, B + B = 10
          B = 5
   Hence, **A = 0, B = 5, C = 1**.
4. 141, 252, 363, 474, 585, 696
   There are **6** three-digit numbers.
5.

   25 m
   ←——→
   ○   ○   ○   ○   ○   ○   ○   ○
   1st 2nd 3rd 4th 5th 6th 7th 8th
   From the 1st to the last (8th) signal lights,
   there are 8 − 1 = 7 intervals.
   Each interval is 25 m.
   7 intervals is 7 × 25 m = 175 m
   The tunnel is **175 m**.
6. To obtain the greatest possible difference,
   the first number must be the greatest
   possible 3-digit number and the second
   number must be the smallest possible
   3-digit number (using the 6 digits given).
   765 − 204 = 561

7.

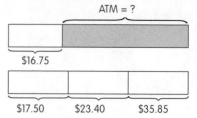

$17.50 + $23.40 + $35.85 = $76.75
$76.75 − $16.75 = $60
Cynthia withdrew **$60** from the ATM.

8. 304 = 33 × 9 + 7

Number of months	Savings
33	$297
34	$306

The number of months he needs to save
is **34**.
9. Look for a 2-digit number that is divisible
   by 6.
   The largest two-digit number is 99,
   followed by 98, 97, 96, …
   99, 98 and 97 are not divisible by 6.
   96 ÷ 6 = 16
   96 is divisible by 6.
   The largest two-digit number is **96**.
10. 1 × 36, 2 × 18, 3 × 12, 4 × 9
    There are **4** ways you can arrange the
    square units.
11. Perimeter of a square = 12 cm
    Length of one side of a square
    = 12 cm ÷ 4 = 3 cm
    The perimeter of the figure is made up of
    18 sides, each of length 3 cm.
    18 × 3 cm = 54 cm
    The perimeter of the figure is **54 cm**.
12. (a)

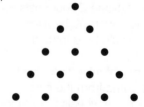

   (b) 1 + 2 + 3 +…+ 9 + 10 = 55
      There are **55** dots in the 10th figure.
   Note:
      1 + 2 + 3 +…+ 8 + 9 + 10
      = (1 + 10) + (2 + 9) + (3 + 8) + (4 + 7) +
        (5 + 6)
      = 5 × 11
      = 55

15 Review Questions 3

Practice Questions (pp. 183-185)

1.

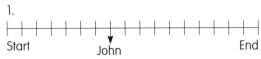

Start   John   End

There were **7** people in line in front of him.

2.

End of Day	Number of meters from the bottom of the well
1	3 – 1 = 2
2	2 + 3 – 1 = 4
3	4 + 3 – 1 = 6
4	6 + 3 – 1 = 8
5	8 + 3 = 11

It will take the snail **5** days to get out of the well.

3. $1,395 – $165 = $1,230
Tracy has **$1,230**.

4. 12:00 midnight $\xrightarrow{-1\,h}$ 11:00 P.M.
$\xrightarrow{-18\,min}$ 10:42 P.M.
The movie must start at **10:42 P.M.**

5. *Before*

Elizabeth		300
Paul		

After

Elizabeth		150
Paul		150

Both have the same number of buttons.

6. Less than 1,000 but greater than 459: it is a three-digit number.
Hundreds digit is even: 4 or <u>6</u> (8 is not possible since the ones digit cannot be 10.)
Ones digit is 2 more than hundreds digit: 6 or <u>8</u> (10 is not possible.)
Tens digit is half of ones digit: 3 or <u>4</u> (3 is impossible since it will work out to be 438 which is less than 459.)
The number is **648**.

7. 10, 5, 2, 2, 2
10 + 5 + 2 + 2 + 2 = 21
The least number of darts needed to achieve that score is **5**.

8. $\boxed{\dfrac{1}{8}} + \boxed{\dfrac{1}{8}} + \boxed{\dfrac{1}{8}} + \boxed{\dfrac{1}{8}} = \dfrac{1}{2}$

Challenging Problems (pp. 189-194)

1. 1 year = 12 months
Amount saved in 1 month = $10
Amount saved in 12 months
= 12 × $10 = $120
$100 + $120 = $220
Jenny will save **$220**.

2. $50 – $38 = $12
The pears cost $12.
$1 can buy 3 pears.
$12 can buy 3 × 12 = 36 pears.
He bought **36** pears.

3. Observe that the "center number" is shared by all four sums, and it must be 5.
1   2   3   4   ⑤   6   7   8   9
The "end numbers" must add up to 15 – 5 = 10.
We look for pairs of numbers whose sum is 10.
(1, 9), (2, 8), (3, 7), (4, 6)

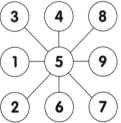

4. A spider has 8 legs, and a snake has 0 legs.
48 ÷ 8 = 6
There are **6** spiders.
22 – 6 = 16
There are **16** snakes.

5. Answers vary. Two examples are:

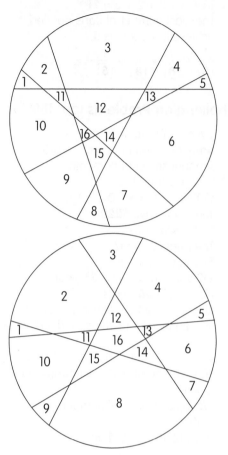

The most number of pieces is **16**.

6. (a) Left circle: $\frac{1}{8} + \frac{1}{8}$

Right circle: $\frac{1}{4}$

$\frac{1}{8} + \frac{1}{8} = \frac{1}{4}$

$\frac{1}{8} = \frac{1}{4} - \frac{1}{\mathbf{4}}$

(b) Left circle: $\frac{3}{6} = \frac{1}{6} + \frac{1}{6} + \frac{1}{6}$

Right circle: $\frac{1}{2}$

$\frac{1}{6} + \frac{1}{6} + \frac{1}{6} = \frac{1}{2}$

$\frac{1}{6} + \frac{1}{6} = \frac{1}{2} - \frac{1}{\mathbf{6}}$

7.

Ann	Jean	Karen	Sue
?	3	2	6

5

15

? + 5 + 6 = 15
? + 11 = 15
? = 15 – 11 = 4
Ann borrowed **4** books.

8. Suppose Lisa bought 11 erasers.
    Then the total cost would be 11 × 40¢ = 440¢.
    The extra 500¢ – 440¢ = 60¢ must have come from the pens.
    A pen costs 50¢ – 40¢ = 10¢ more than an eraser.
    60¢ ÷ 10¢ = 6
    She bought 6 pens.
    11 – 6 = 5
    (a) She bought **5** erasers.
         6 × 50¢ = 300¢ = $3.00.
    (b) The total cost of the pens is **$3.00**.

9. Observe that the length of one rectangle is 4 times its width.

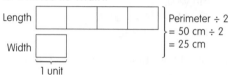

    5 units = 25 cm
    1 unit = 25 cm ÷ 5 = 5 cm
    4 units = 4 × 5 cm = 20 cm
    Length of one rectangle = 20 cm
    Length of square = Length of rectangle
                     = 20 cm
    The length of the square is **20 cm**.

10. If all 13 children drank 3 cups each, then they would consume 13 × 3 = 39 cups.
    The extra 46 – 39 = 7 cups must have come from the boys, who each drank 4 cups each.
    Each boy drank 4 – 3 = 1 more cup than each girl.
    7 ÷ 1 = 7
    13 – 7 = 6
    There were **7** boys and **6** girls.

11. Length of the original wire
    = Sum of the two perimeters
    = (5 cm + 9 cm + 5 cm + 9 cm) + (10 cm + 6 cm + 10 cm + 6 cm)
    = 28 cm + 32 cm
    = 60 cm
    The length of the original wire is **60 cm**.

12. There are **16** right angles in the figure.

Blank

Blank

Blank

Blank